Dissection of the cat

(AND COMPARISONS WITH MAN)

A laboratory manual on *Felis domestica*

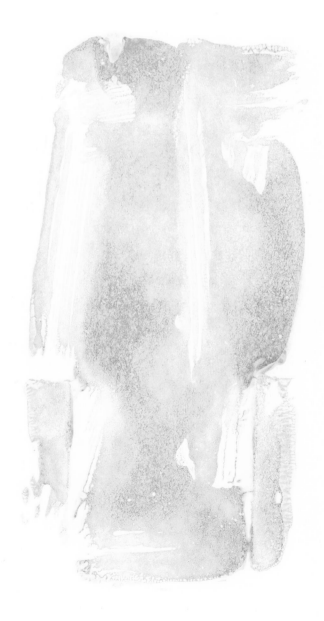

Dissection of the cat

(AND COMPARISONS WITH MAN)

A laboratory manual on *Felis domestica*

BRUCE M. HARRISON, Ph.D., Sc.D., LL.D.

Emeritus Professor of Zoology, The University of Southern California;
Emeritus Associate Professor of Anatomy, California College
of Medicine; formerly at Iowa State University

Sixth edition

Saint Louis

THE C. V. MOSBY COMPANY

1970

Preface

This book is written for courses in human anatomy where the human body is not available for dissection by the student. The primary objective of the book is to give the student a thorough understanding of anatomy, not only of the cat, but especially of man. Many changes and additions have been made to attain this goal for this edition and to enable the student to grasp more easily what is to be learned.

All illustrations of the cat have been redone and modernized. Those of man are the same as in the former edition. The essential structures of all illustrations have been labeled and several illustrations have been simplified.

Many sections have been rewritten and clarified to give more information about man. The review questions have been reevaluated and many changed.

Many more comparisons of the anatomy of the cat and man are included; more embryological and physiological explanations are given; more emphasis is placed on anomalies and their more probable and significant interpretation. In addition, more specific directions on dissecting have been given, and more facts supporting the theories of recapitulation and evolution are included. It is believed that the book is now more meaningful and dynamic than were previous editions.

Some of the foregoing changes were effected because the time allowed for laboratory work has been shortened in most colleges and universities. Thus, it is necessary to present the methods of dissecting and the facts of anatomy more clearly. The student's emphasis in time and thought should be placed on the actual specimen, rather than in trying to find the right name and then trying to locate it at the right place on an illustration. Also, the student has a right to know in advance what kind of questions may be asked of him in future tests and examinations.

Appreciation is hereby expressed to my former students, associates, and those instructors who have expressed their constructive criticisms.

Appreciation is also expressed to Mr. John Plunkett and Mr. Jim Conahan for redoing the illustrations, and especially to my wife, Lessie C. Harrison, for typing, proofreading, and many helpful suggestions.

Bruce M. Harrison

Contents

3 General internal organs of the cat, 96

4 Venous and lymphatic systems of the cat, 121

5 Arterial system and heart of the cat, 139

Dissection of the cat

(AND COMPARISONS WITH MAN)

A laboratory manual on *Felis domestica*

1

Skeleton of the cat

INTRODUCTION

Each student should be issued a box containing about twenty of the larger representative cat bones. Select the following bones from your set and find their proper position on the drawing of the skeleton (Fig. 1). The first two vertebrae are the **atlas** and **axis**, respectively. The **thoracic vertebrae,** to which the **true** and **false ribs** are attached, are situated in the chest. The first nine ribs are called **true ribs,** since each has its own **cartilage** attaching it to the sternum. The last four ribs are called **false ribs,** since each does not have its own attachment to the sternum. The last of the false ribs is also called a **floating rib,** since it has no cartilage attaching it to the sternum. The lower ends of the ribs join the sternum; the anterior or front bone of the sternum is the **manubrium,** followed by several **body** or **sternebrae bones,** and the posterior portion, the **xiphoid** or **ensiform process.** Next in the spinal column are the **lumbar vertebrae** in the small of the back, then the **sacrum,** consisting of three vertebrae, to which the **ilium,** or hip bone, is attached. The tail bones are the **caudal** or **coccygeal vertebrae.** There are usually a few remnants of hemal arches, known as **chevron bones,** on the lower surface of the fourth, fifth, and sixth caudal vertebrae.

The **clavicle** is a small bone anterior to the lower end of the **scapula,** and the

---

A shorter discussion of the anatomy of the cat is given in Harrison, B. H.: *Manual of Comparative Anatomy*, ed. 3, 1970, The C. V. Mosby Co.

hyoid is posterior to the lower jaw. These bones may be seen on a well-mounted skeleton. The anterior, or foreleg, bones consist of the following: **humerus, radius, ulna, carpals** (wrist bones), **metacarpals** (palm-of-the-hand bones), and **phalanges** (finger or toe bones).

The bones of the posterior limb or leg are as follows: **femur, patella** (kneecap), **tibia, fibula, tarsals** (ankle and heel bones), **metatarsals** (instep bones), and **phalanges** (toe bones). Arrange the skull and the representative bones of the spinal column in a straight line with the head farthest away. Determine whether each of the remaining bones belongs to the right or left side and place it in its proper position on the right or the left of the vertebrae representing the spinal column. Refer to the mounted skeleton for aid in determining whether or not a given bone is the right or the left.

Compare Figs. 1 and 2 and observe that the skeletons of cat and man are constructed on the same general plan. If you place the mounted cat's skeleton up on its hind legs or place the mounted human skeleton on its hands and knees and compare them, the close similarity of structure will be much more evident and striking.

DORSAL VIEW OF SKULL (Fig. 3)

Look in the back of the manual for definitions of many of the technical terms used.

Observe the **premaxillary bones** at the sides of the **external nasal apertures.** These bones bear the **incisor teeth.** How many are

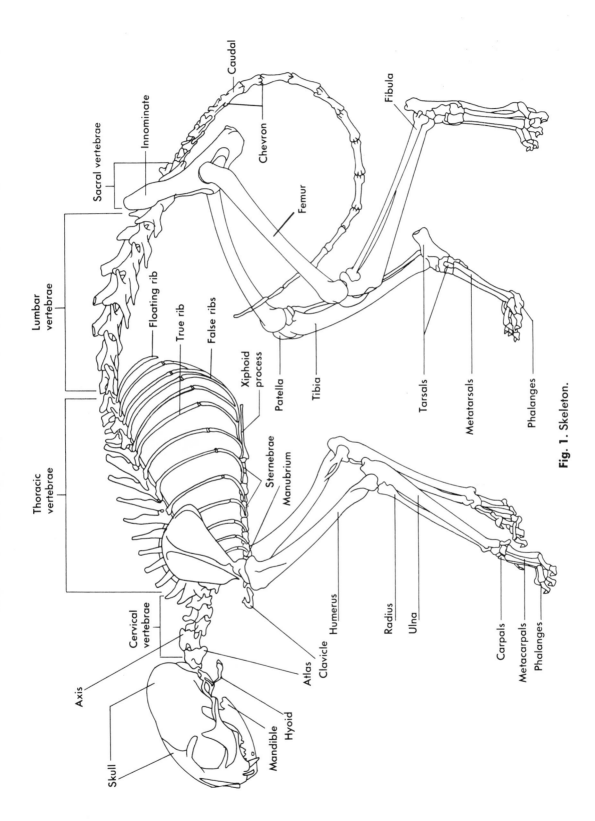

Fig. 1. Skeleton.

Caudal

Chevron

Fibula

Femur

Sacral vertebrae

Innominate

Lumbar vertebrae

Floating rib

True rib

False ribs

Xiphoid process

Patella

Tibia

Tarsals

Metatarsals

Phalanges

Thoracic vertebrae

Sternebrae

Manubrium

Cervical vertebrae

Humerus

Radius

Ulna

Carpals

Metacarpals

Phalanges

Axis

Atlas

Clavicle

Skull

Mandible

Hyoid

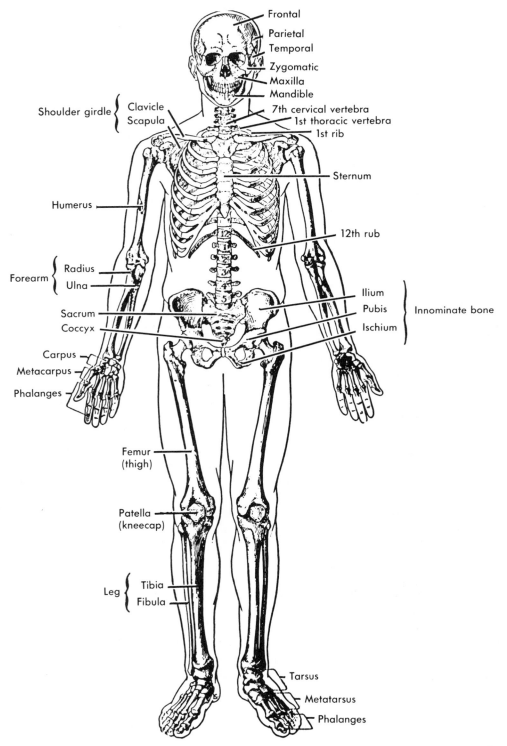

Fig. 2. Anterior view of the human skeleton. (From Millard, N. D., King, B. G., and Showers, M. J.: Human anatomy and physiology, Philadelphia, 1956, W. B. Saunders Co.)

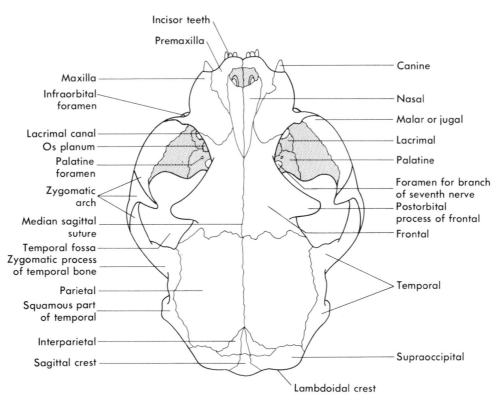

Fig. 3. Skull, dorsal view.

there? At each side of the middorsal line, immediately caudal to the nasal apertures, are the **nasal bones.** Lateral to these and also to the premaxillary bones are the **maxillary bones.** Each maxillary normally bears one **canine,** three premolars, and one small molar. Farther posterior on the dorsal surface are the **frontal bones,** which meet one another along the **middorsal suture** and project laterally as the **postorbital** or **zygomatic process** of the frontal bone.

The orbit of the eye is bounded laterally by the **malar,** or **jugal, bone,** sometimes also called the zygomatic bone, which bears at its caudal extremity the **postorbital,** or **frontal, process** of the malar, directed toward the postorbital process of the **frontal bone,** mentioned in the previous paragraph. The malar or jugal bone joins posteriorly with the **zygomatic process** of the **temporal bone** to form the **zygomatic arch.** The **orbit of the eye** and the **temporal fossa** are bounded laterally by the **zygomatic arch.**

Posterior to each frontal bone, meeting one another along the middorsal line, is a

parietal bone, and lateral to each of these is the **squamosal portion of the temporal bone.** Posterior to and slightly between the parietals sometimes may be seen a small **interparietal bone,** and caudal to it is the **supraoccipital bone.** This latter bone bears a transverse ridge, known as the **lambdoid crest,** for the attachment of the muscles of the dorsal part of the neck, and it also bears a **dorsal median sagittal crest,** which extends forward between the parietals.

Within the limits of the orbit of the eye may be seen, when viewed from above, a portion of the **palatine bone** with two small openings, the palatine foramina. The more lateral opening is for the **passage of the palatine branch of the facial nerve,** and the median opening is for the **sphenopalatine branch** of the same nerve. These foramina can be seen better in ventral view. Anterior to the **palatine bone** is the **lacrimal bone,** which also bears an opening at its median border, the **lacrimal canal,** through which pass the tears or secretion of the lacrimal gland into the nasal cham-

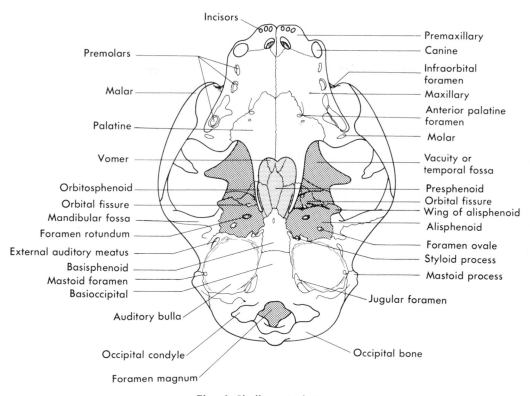

Fig. 4. Skull, ventral view.

Labels on figure:
Incisors — Premaxillary — Canine — Infraorbital foramen — Maxillary — Anterior palatine foramen — Molar — Vacuity or temporal fossa — Presphenoid — Orbital fissure — Wing of alisphenoid — Alisphenoid — Foramen ovale — Styloid process — Mastoid process — Jugular foramen — Occipital bone

Premolars — Malar — Palatine — Vomer — Orbitosphenoid — Orbital fissure — Mandibular fossa — Foramen rotundum — External auditory meatus — Basisphenoid — Mastoid foramen — Basioccipital — Auditory bulla — Occipital condyle — Foramen magnum

SUTURES OF SKULL

ber. The part of the maxillary bone anterior to and below the front of the eye contains the large **infraorbital foramen** for the passage of the infraorbital nerves and blood vessels. These nerves are branches of the maxillary branch of the **fifth**, or **trigeminal**, **nerve**. On the anterior median wall of the orbit, bounded by the **frontal, lacrimal**, and **palatine bones**, is the **os planum**, which is a part of the **ethmoid bone** and forms part of the **socket**, or **orbit**. Other bones of the orbit, which cannot be seen in the dorsal view (Fig. 3), will be considered later.

SUTURES OF SKULL

The bones of the skull are joined by means of immovable articulations, known as **sutures**. These sutures are designated by combining names of the bones between which they are situated, such as **nasomaxillary suture** between the nasal and maxillary bones. Often, when a suture separates the two corresponding bones of opposite sides, the prefix "inter" is used, such as the **inter-** **maxillary suture** between the maxillaries, which shows on the ventral surface. The sutures bounding the parietal bone, however, have not been named by this system. The suture caudad to or behind the parietals, separating them from the occipital, is known as the **lambdoid suture.** Separating the parietals and squamous portions of the temporal bones is the **squamous suture,** and the transverse suture separating the two parietals from the two frontals is the **coronal suture.** Separating the two nasals, the two frontals, and the two parietals is the **median sagittal suture.**

VENTRAL VIEW OF SKULL (Fig. 4)

As you make this study, it would be most helpful to have the disarticulated, or individual, bones of the skull to examine also.

Examine the lower or ventral surface of a skull. The **premaxillary bones** almost surround the **foramina incisiva**, or **anterior palatine foramina.** The limiting sutures may be difficult to determine in an adult skull. The **premaxillary bones** bear the **incisor teeth.** The **maxillary bones** are immediately posterior, meeting one another along the midventral line, and in the fully developed specimen each bears one **canine,** three **premolars,** and one small **molar.** The **palatine bones** are caudad to the **maxillary bones,** and parts of them form the roof of the mouth, known as the hard palate. Sometimes, in the embryonic stage of man, the palatine bone from one side does not come across and meet its mate from the other side, resulting in a **cleft palate.** So far as is known, this does not occur in the cat. The **vomer bone** lies dorsal to the median line of the maxillary and palatine bones and helps separate the two **nasal chambers;** in man the vomer pushes up into the cranial chamber, separating parts of the **cerebral hemisphere** of the **cerebrum.** The flattened part of the vomer may be seen by looking into the posterior nasal openings. The soft palate, which is membranous, lies posterior to the bony part and separates the anterior part of the pharynx into the **nasopharynx** and the **stomodeal part.** The **presphenoid bone** may be seen as a small, elongated bone along the median line caudad to the vomer, forming part of the roof of the pharynx and nasal passage. Lateral to the presphenoid bone is the pterygoid process of the sphenoid, also forming part of the roof and sides of the pharynx and extending backward and downward as long, slender projections about one-half inch apart. Each sharp point is a hamular process of the pterygoid. Within the posteromedian wall of each orbit lie two distinct portions of the sphenoid region, which may be seen if a fairly young skull is examined. The shorter and anterior of the two is the **orbitosphenoid bone,** or lesser wing, and the other is the **alisphenoid bone,** or greater wing. The former contains the most anterior of a group of four foramina in this region. This is the **optic foramen,** for the passage of the optic nerve.

The **alisphenoid bone** lies lateral and ventral to the orbit of the eye with its base posterior to the orbitosphenoid. It forms the posterior wall for the foramen caudad to the optic foramen. This opening is the **orbital fissure,** through which pass the **third** (motor oculus), the **fourth** (pathetic or trochlear), the **sixth** (abducent), and the ophthalmic branch of the **fifth** (trigeminal) cranial nerves. The **optic foramen** and the **orbital fissure** may not show in a strict ventral view. The greater wing of the alisphenoid bone projects dorsally and laterally as a long process between the lateral edges of the frontal and temporal bones and joins a ventrally directed process from the parietal.

The **presphenoid** and the two **orbitosphenoids** are fused into one bone, while the **basisphenoid** and the two **alisphenoids** are fused with one another in the cat. In man, these six bones are all fused into one bone and are called the **sphenoid.** The fusion of bones is a sign of advancement and indicates, in this small way, that man is higher than the cat. Examine these parts (if available) on **disarticulated** skulls of cat and man.

The **basisphenoid** lies caudad to the presphenoid along the midventral line. About halfway from this midventral line on the **basisphenoid** to the articulating **mandibular fossa** for the lower jaw is the **foramen ovale;** anterior and median to it is the **foramen rotundum.** The foramen ovale is for the passage of the mandibular branch of the fifth, or trigeminal, nerve, and the foramen rotundum is for the maxillary branch of the trigemial. The last two foramnia complete the series of four mentioned previously, and they are on the proximal portion of the alisphenoid bone. Lateral to the foramen ovale is a transverse depression, the **mandibular fossa,** for the articulation of the lower jaw. Fit the jaw into this depression.

The large, oval prominences posterior to the mandibular fossae are the **tympanic** or **auditory bullae,** which are probably for the amplification of sound. Between them is the **basioccipital bone.** The large **foramen magnum** is at the posterior end of the skull and through it passes the spinal cord. The **occipital condyles** are prominences on each side of the foramen magnum and close to it. These rub against or articulate on the first vertebra of the spinal column. This vertebra is the **atlas.**

Close to the inner surface of the posterior extremity of the tympanic bulla is the large **jugular foramen** for the passage of the ninth, tenth, and eleventh nerves. On the anterolateral surface of the bulla is the external auditory meatus, which leads to the tympanic membrane. Posterior to this are one or two small **stylomastoid foramina.** The small **mastoid process** of the **temporal bone** projects forward, almost covering one small foramen. At the craniomedial angle of the tympanic bulla, projecting ventrally forward and medially, is the **styloid process.** Just anterior to this process is a **foramen for the exit of the eustachian tube** from the middle ear. Only a portion of the **ethmoid bone** can be seen in the complete skull. This part constitutes the **turbinals,** or **turbinate bones,** which project into the nasal chamber.

LEFT LATERAL VIEW OF SKULL (Fig. 5)

Keep in mind the parts that you will see in the lateral view that you identified in the ventral view study. The **occipital condyles** project ventrally near the posterior part of the skull. Above these condyles is the **lambdoid crest** or ridge that passes toward the **auditory meatus,** which is the large opening on the lateral surface of the **tympanic bulla.** The lambdoid crest becomes continuous with the **zygomatic process** of the **temporal** and **zygomatic arch.** On the caudal surface of the bulla is the small **jugular process** of the occipital bone, a short distance lateral to the occipital condyles. Anterior to this process, about halfway to the auditory meatus, is the much larger **mastoid process.** One or two **stylomastoid foramina,** for the passage of branches of the seventh cranial nerve, lie anterior or ventral to the mastoid process. If the skull is not thoroughly cleaned, these small openings may not be seen. Within the opening of the auditory meatus and median to the tympanic membrane are the small ear bones, the **malleus, incus,** and **stapes.** These cannot be seen unless the bone is cut away, which may be done later.

The foramen for the passage of the **lacrimal duct** is at the anterolateral edge of

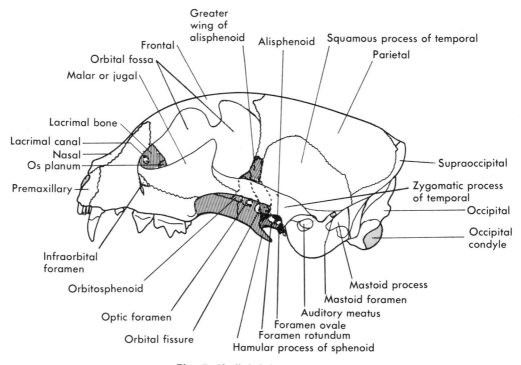

Fig. 5. Skull, left lateral view.

Greater wing of alisphenoid
Frontal
Orbital fossa
Malar or jugal
Alisphenoid
Squamous process of temporal
Parietal
Lacrimal bone
Lacrimal canal
Nasal
Os planum
Premaxillary
Supraoccipital
Zygomatic process of temporal
Occipital
Occipital condyle
Infraorbital foramen
Orbitosphenoid
Optic foramen
Orbital fissure
Mastoid process
Mastoid foramen
Auditory meatus
Foramen ovale
Foramen rotundum
Hamular process of sphenoid

the **lacrimal bone**, and the **infraorbital foramen** may also be seen in the lateral view. Posterior to the lacrimal and below the frontal a part of the **palatine bone** may be observed containing two openings, the outer and smaller (the **palatine foramen**) for the passage of the **palatine branch of the facial nerve** and the larger and median (the **sphenopalatine foramen**) for the **sphenopalatine branch** of the same nerve. These openings are the ends of the posterior palatine canals. The other smaller ends are in the roof of the mouth in or near the suture separating the maxillary and palatine bones. A small part of the **ethmoid bone**, known as the **os planum**, forms a part of the anteromedian wall of the orbit between the **frontal**, **lacrimal**, and **palatine bones**.

MEDIAN SAGITTAL VIEW OF SKULL (Fig. 6)

Examine the half skull. Do you have the right or the left half? The skulls that have been soaked in formalin hold the bones together much better than the fresh specimens; hence these are sawed in half for this study. We now wish to see the relationships between the bones of the skull and the larger parts of the brain. Observe that the cranial cavity is partially divided by a bony partition or septum, which extends median-ward from the parietal bone. This is the

tentorium, which is unossified in man. The larger and quite irregular cavity anterior to the **tentorium** is filled almost entirely by the **cerebrum**, with a **fossa for the olfactory blubs**, filling the comparatively small area against the nasal chamber. The **cribriform plate**, which is a part of the ethmoid bone, separates the nasal and cranial chambers, and through it pass many olfactory nerves from the olfactory bulbs onto the **turbinals** or **turbinate bones** of the nose. There are three of these turbinals or **conchae** in man, projecting into each nasal chamber from the lateral wall. The upper two are **ethmoturbinals**, and the lower is the **maxilloturbinal**. These turbinal bones are much more complicated in the cat than in man. This gives relatively more surface for nerve endings, which probably accounts in part for the keener sense of smell in the cat.

The lowest depression on the median plane of the skull, anterior to the lower end of the **tentorium**, is the **sella turcica**, or **pituitary fossa**, in which is lodged the **pituitary endocrinal gland**. Immediately dorsal to this gland is the **diencephalon** of the brain. Above the olfactory bulbs the **frontal sinus** may be seen, providing the skull has been cut slightly to one side of the median plane.

This cavity is in the frontal bone. Anterior and lateral to it on each side is the

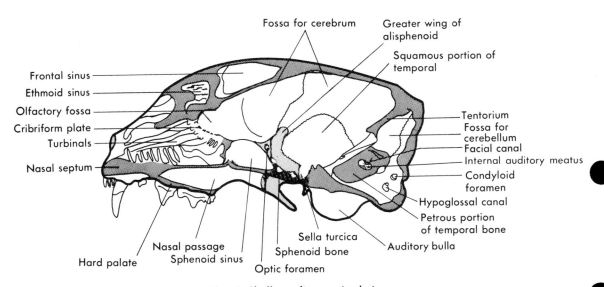

Fig. 6. Skull, median sagittal view.

ethmoid sinus, which is dorsal to the nasal chamber and contains the superior turbinal bones or cartilages.

The ethmoid sinus is relatively larger in the cat than in man, as is also the maxillary. The latter is not shown in Fig. 6. It is believed that these sinuses drain better in animals that carry the body and head in a horizontal position. Man is more prone to sinus trouble. The turbinal bones, or conchae, are projections that curve from the lateral walls into each nasal chamber. Each concha has many folds, and each contains the oldfactory nerve endings for the sense of smell and many blood vessels for warming and moistening the air. The nose is an air conditioner for the lungs.

The cavity behind the tentorium is largely occupied by the cerebellum and the medulla oblongata. In the lower lateral wall of the skull, which surrounds the cerebellum, is the petrosal portion of the temporal bone, which has an irregular inner surface and often a slightly different color. It contains the semicircular canals and the cochlea. The latter contains the organ of Corti of the inner ear. The inner surface of the petrous portion of the temporal bone is stippled in the drawing (Fig. 6) and has two depressions. Within the lower depression are two foramina. The more dorsal of the two is the canalis facialis for the passage of a branch of the seventh nerve, and the ventral foramen is the internal auditory meatus for the passage of the eighth (auditory) nerve. The upper depression on the inner surface of the petrosal part has no foramina and is of no special significance. In the lateral wall of the foramen magnum are two foramina; the lower is the hypoglossal canal, and the more dorsal is the condyloid foramen. Above and anterior to the hamular process and the palatine bone is the internal naris and above it, the sphenoid sinus. There is some evidence from a comparative study of the nerves and vertebrae of various animals that the skull has been derived by a fusion of vertebrae.

There are two principal kinds or types of bones in the skull that differ in their embryological development.

1. The membranous dermal (superficial) bones develop directly from loose connective tissue. These are the premaxillary, maxillary, malar or jugal, palatine, lacrimal, nasal, frontal, parietal, and interparietal bones of the skull.

2. The endochondral (cartilaginous or deep) bones of the skull are the vomer, presphenoid, basisphenoid, orbitosphenoid, alisphenoid, basioccipital, ethmoid, and ethmoturbinal. These are preformed in cartilage. The occipital and the temporal bones are each a combination of the two types of bone. The supraoccipital part of the occipital is membranous, and the occipital condyles are endochondral. In the temporal bone the process of the temporal, which forms the posterior half of the zygomatic arch, and the large, curved squamous portion are membranous, while the petrosal portion and the bulla are endochondral. Both the membranous and endochondral types have haversian systems when fully formed; they cannot be distinguished histologically when fully formed.

FORAMINA OF SKULL

1. The foramen magnum is the large opening in the occipital bone for the passage of the spinal cord to join the medulla oblongata of the brain. The spinal accessory nerves and the vertebral arteries also pass through this opening.

2. The hypoglossal canal passes through the exoccipital bone at the inside lower portion of the foramen magnum, opens on the ventral surface with the jugular foramen, and transmits the hypoglossal nerve.

3. The condyloid canal opens on the inside upper part of the occipital condyle and transmits a vein from the transverse sinus.

4. The jugular foramen is at the junction of the auditory bulla, exoccipital, and basioccipital bones in the posteromedian surface of the bulla. It transmits the inferior cerebral vein and the ninth, tenth, and eleventh nerves.

5. The stylomastoid foramen is between the stylomastoid process and the lateral caudal border of the bulla. It serves as

a passage for a **branch of the seventh nerve.**

6. The **facial canal,** or **aqueduct of Fallopii,** passes through the median part of the petrous portion of the temporal bone. It is the principal exit for branches of the **facial nerve.**

7. The **internal auditory meatus** is below the facial canal on the median surface of the petrous and serves as a passage for the **eighth,** or **auditory, nerve** from the brain into the inner ear.

8. The **external auditory meatus** is on the lateral surface of the auditory bulla for the entrance of sound waves to the tympanum.

9. The **foramen for the eustachian tube** is lateral to the styloid process at the anterior edge of the auditory bulla.

10. The **foramen ovale** is at the basal posterior edge of the alisphenoid bone, median to the mandibular fossa. It transmits the mandibular branch of the **trigeminal nerve, the accessory meningeal artery,** and a **branch of the external carotid artery.**

11. The **foramen rotundum** is in the base of the alisphenoid, anterior and slightly median to the foramen ovale, and serves as a passage for the **maxillary branch of the trigeminal nerve.**

12. The **orbital fissure** is between the bases of the orbitosphenoid and alisphenoid bones. Through this fissure pass the **third, fourth,** and **sixth cranial nerves** and the **ophthalmic branch of the fifth.**

13. The **optic foramen** is in the base of the orbitosphenoid bone and transmits the **optic nerve.**

14. The **olfactory foramina** pass through the cribiform plate of the ethmoid bone and permit the **olfactory nerves** to spread out on the turbinal bones of the nasal cavity.

15. The **sphenopalatine foramen** is the larger and more median of the two in the palatine bone of the ventromedian wall of the orbit of the eye. It transmits the **sphenopalatine artery** and the **posterior superior nasal nerve,** which is a branch of the fifth, or trigeminal, nerve.

16. The **posterior palatine canal** is lateral to the sphenopalatine foramen and passes through to the anterolateral edge of the palatine bone on the ventral surface of the hard palate. It transmits the **greater palatine nerve** and the **descending palatine artery.**

17. The **anterior palatine foramen** is on each side of the median line, between the bases of the canine teeth, and is bounded by the premaxillary and maxillary bones. The **nasopalatine nerve,** which is a branch of the maxillary, passes through it.

18. The **infraorbital foramen** is in the maxillary bone, below and anterior to the eye. It is large and transmits the **superior maxillary nerve.** Sometimes two foramina are present instead of one, depending on where the nerve branches.

19. The **lacrimal canal** is between the lacrimal and maxillary bones in the anteromedian wall of the orbit. The **lacrimal duct** passes through it on the way to the nasal chamber.

SOME DIFFERENCES IN SKULLS OF CAT AND MAN

1. Man has twenty-two separate skull bones, whereas the cat has thirty-five to forty.

2. Frontal and parietal bones are enlarged and pushed higher in man, whereas the jaws are relatively smaller and less protruding than those in the cat.

3. The premaxilla and maxilla on each side fuse into one bone in man but are separate in the cat.

4. The two frontal bones that are separate in embryo man become fused in the adult, but they remain separate in the adult cat.

5. The several parts of the sphenoid are fused into one bone in man but are in two principal parts in the adult cat.

6. The ossified dura mater forms a part of the parietal bone known as the **tentorium** in the cat but remains unossified in man.

7. A part of the hyoid branchial arch ossifies and forms the part of the temporal bone known as the **styloid process** in man but is not so formed in the cat.

8. The **lambdoid crest** and the **auditory**

bulla are well formed in the cat but are absent in man.

9. An interparietal is often present as a separate bone in the cat but is only occasionally found in man.

10. The posterolateral wall of the orbit of the eye is well ossified in man but is only partially ossified in the cat.

11. Each half of the upper jaw of the cat has three incisors, one canine, three premolars, and one molar, whereas man has two, one, two, and three, respectively.

12. The inferior nasal **conchae** of man are separate bones, whereas in the cat these are parts of the maxillary bones, the maxilloturbinals or ventral nasal conchae.

13. The mandibles of the cat are easily separated from one another at the **symphysis,** whereas in man they are strongly fused.

14. The cat normally has **thirteen pairs** of ribs, but occasionally there are fourteen or even fifteen pairs. These extra ribs appear adjacent to the **seventh cervical vertebra,** adjacent to the **first lumbar vertebra,** or at both of these locations. In man there are usually **twelve pairs** of ribs, but extra pairs may appear at the same locations as mentioned for the cat. An abnormal or unusual structure such as this, which appears suddenly in an animal and is not present in its ancestors for several generations, is called an "anomaly." This anomaly, when it occurs in man, by the first lumbar vertebra, is called a "gorilla" rib, since it is more often found in the gorilla. When you come to a scientific or technical term and you are not sure of its meaning, look in the back of the book for its definition.

Name _____

Date _____

REVIEW QUESTIONS ON SKULL

The student should answer all questions and hand them to the instructor for evaluation.

1. What are the two principal types or kinds of bones in the skull?

2. What are the names of two cartilaginous bones of the skull?

3. Name two membranous bones of the skull.

4. Name the bones that help form the cranial cavity. (Figs. 5 and 6)

5. What is the general position of most of the foramina of the skull? (Fig. 4)

6. What bones help to form the orbit of the eye? (Figs. 5 and 6)

7. What is the explanation of the cleft palate?

8. Name and locate six foramina. (Fig. 4)

9. Within what bone are the parts of the inner and middle ear? (Fig. 6)

10. Locate and state the significance of the cribriform plate. (Fig. 6)

11. Name two air sinuses seen in the median sagittal section of the skull. (Fig. 6)

12. State five differences in the structure of the skulls of cat and man. Answer from your own observations.

13. About how many foramina are there in a cat's skull? (Fig. 4)

14. What structures usually pass through foramina?

15. What bones form the roof of the mouth? (Fig. 4)

16. What is an anomaly?

17. What bones constitute a zygomatic arch? (Figs. 3 and 5)

18. What structure helps to separate the cavities for the cerebrum and cerebellum? (Fig. 6)

19. What bones contain air sinuses? (Fig. 6)

20. What bones help to form the nasal passage? (Figs. 4 and 5)

LOWER JAW, OR MANDIBLE (Fig. 7)

If you have two halves of the lower jaw, they were probably taken from different cats. Do you have the right or left jaw? Fit the jaw onto the skull. Examine the inner surface of one-half of the lower jaw. The two halves are joined in the median line at their anterior extremities. This area of fusion is called the **symphysis**. Each half jaw consists of a horizontal portion, the **body**, bearing teeth on its alveolar border and an ascending portion, the **ramus**. In each half of the lower jaw there are three **incisors**, one **canine**, two **premolars**, and one **molar**, provided all are present. How do these teeth differ? The space between the canine and the first premolar is the **diastema**. Caudally the ramus is divided into a **condyloid process**, which extends transversely and fits into the mandibular fossa to articulate with the skull, and a long, vertical **coronoid process**, to which the masseter muscle is attached. The lower proximal projection is the **angular process**. On the outer distal portion of the body are one or more mental foramina, which are the openings of the mandibular canal. This canal extends diagonally through each half jaw for the passage of the inferior alveolar artery and nerve. The latter is a subdivision of the mandibular branch of the seventh nerve. A small wire may be passed through some mandibular canals. The proximal end of the mandibular canal opens by a **mandibular foramen** on the inner surface of the ramus, near the base of the condyloid process. Above this process is the **superior notch** and below it is the **inferior notch** of the mandible. In man the two halves of the mandible are united at their cephalic ends to form a single bone. In the cat the two halves are separate but articulate closely at the **symphysis menti** by a thin interarticular cartilage. After the study of each cat bone compare it with that of man, if the human bone is available.

Dental formula of the cat (*Felis*):

$$i\,\frac{3}{3},\, c\,\frac{1}{1},\, pm\,\frac{3}{2},\, m\,\frac{1}{1}\ \text{totals 30}$$

Dental formula of man (*Homo*):

$$i\,\frac{2}{2},\, c\,\frac{1}{1},\, pm\,\frac{2}{2},\, m\,\frac{3}{3}\ \text{totals 32}$$

Extra teeth (beyond the normal number) are seldom seen in the cat but are not so uncommon in man. They appear in the upper jaw, sometimes almost a complete double set. This condition is called an "anomaly" and is interpreted as an **atavistic character**, a return or "harping back" to a remote ancestral condition.

PECTORAL GIRDLE (Figs. 1 and 8)

The **scapula**, or shoulder blade, is held in place by muscles and articulates with the

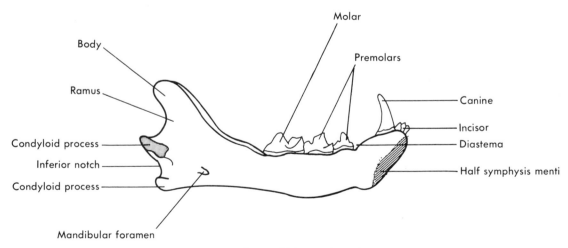

Fig. 7. Left mandible, median view.

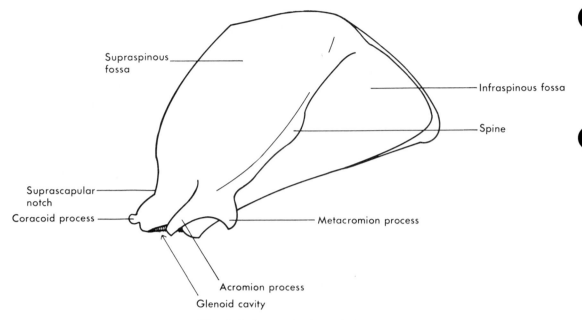

Supraspinous fossa

Infraspinous fossa

Spine

Suprascapular notch

Coracoid process

Metacromion process

Acromion process

Glenoid cavity

Fig. 8. Left scapula, lateral view.

humerus. The **clavicle** is small and does not reach the scapula; in man it is relatively larger. On the lateral surface of the scapula is a long ridge, the **spine of the scapula,** which separates the **supraspinous fossa** from the **infraspinous fossa.** The spine has two projections at its lower extremity: the **acromion process,** which extends toward the **glenoid cavity** (socket for the humerus), and the **metacromion process,** a flat, posteriorly directed process a short distance up on the spine. Near the upper inner edge of the glenoid cavity is the **coracoid process of the scapula,** which is short and curved. Immediately above the coracoid process on the cephalic edge is the **suprascapular notch.**

As you work on cat bones compare them with those of man, if they are available. The **coracoid process** is vestigial in the cat and man but is a well-developed bone in most reptiles and in the bird, in which it is large and braces the shoulder. The shape of the scapula is well suited for the attachment of many muscles, which will be studied later.

HUMERUS (Fig. 9)

The proximal, or upper, end of the humerus is larger than the distal end and con-

sists of a smooth, rounded central portion, the **head** and a lateral **greater tuberosity,** which is separated from the head and **lesser tuberosity** by the **bicipital groove.** These parts constitute the **proximal epiphysis,** the lower limit of which is the **epiphyseal line.** The **shaft,** or **diaphysis,** forms most of the long, median smooth part, with the **supracondyloid foramen** near the median edge and distal extremity. On the cephalic surface of the shaft is the **pectoral ridge,** which extends distally from the anterior limit of the greater tuberosity down the cephalic surface. The **deltoid ridge** extends from the lateral limits of the greater tuberosity distally and forward across the lateral surface to join the pectoral ridge. On the median surface, two-thirds of the distance from the proximal end, is a small **nutrient foramen** for the entrance of a blood vessel. This is often difficult to locate. At the distal end on the posterior surface is a definite depression, the **olecranon fossa,** into which the olecranon process of the ulna fits each time the foreleg is extended. The **distal articulating epiphysis** consists of the large, sharp-edged, circular **trochlea** and the small, rounded **capitulum.** The **supracondyloid arch** forms the inner boundary of the **supra-**

16

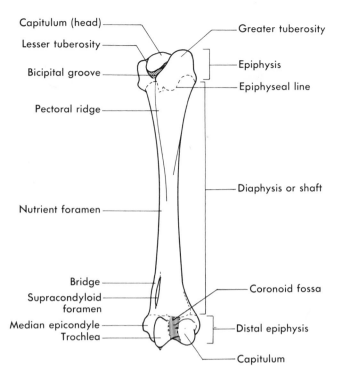

Fig. 9. Cephalic view of left humerus.

condyloid foramen, which is absent in man. The **median epicondyle** is distal and median to the arch.

From the foregoing description determine whether you have the right or the left humerus and compare it with the mounted cat's skeleton. Each long bone of the forelimbs and hind limbs consists of an elongated **shaft,** or **diaphysis,** and at each end an enlarged articulating portion, the **epiphysis.** In early life these epiphyses are separated from the diaphysis by cartilage that continues to proliferate cells long after birth, which accounts for much of the increase in height during growth. Often, when the bones of a young animal are boiled to clean them, the epiphyses fall off, as may be noticed on some of the bones being studied. At the upper end of the fully developed humerus this area of growth is often easily seen and is known as the **epiphyseal plate,** or **line.**

RADIUS (Fig. 10)

The radius and ulna constitute the bones of the **forearm.** The smaller extremity of the radius is the proximal end, or **head,**

which contains a slight depression for the articulation with the lateral **capitulum** of the humerus. These bones are not in actual contact but are separated by synovial fluid. The depression has a rounded **tuberosity** at its lateral edge. The slight constriction distal to the head is the **neck,** and immediately beyond it is the **tubercle,** which projects posteriorly toward the ulna. The **distal epiphysis** is larger than the proximal epiphysis and sometimes is easily separated from the **diaphysis,** or **shaft,** which is slightly concave on its posterior surface. Laterally, an **articulating facet** rubs against the ulna. The **distal epiphysis** possesses three grooves on its anterior surface for the passage of the extensor muscles of the forearm. The median portion of this epiphysis also has a small, sharp **tuberosity.**

ULNA (Fig. 11)

The ulna has a large **semilunar notch** into which most of the distal end of the humerus articulates. The median edge of the notch is the smoother, since the lateral edge has a projection and a smaller radial notch for the head of the radius. The

17

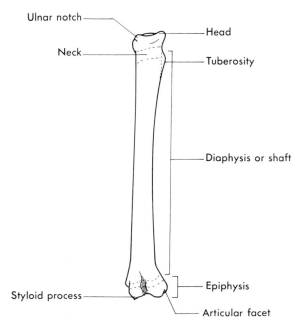

Fig. 10. Cephalic view of left radius.

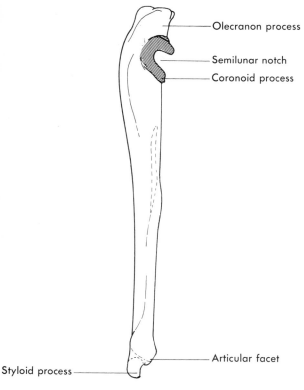

Fig. 11. Median view of left ulna.

18

coronoid process projects distally from the lower ends of both notches. The large extention of the ulna at the elbow beyond the semilunar notch is the **olecranon process.** At the distal end of the ulna is the blunt-pointed **styloid process,** which has a slightly concave median surface. The short projection near the base of the **styloid process** is the **articular facet,** for articulation with the radius. The styloid process represents the epiphysis, which if not well ossified may have come off when cleaning the bones.

From the foregoing description determine whether you have the right or the left ulna. If the humerus, radius, and ulna of your set are from the same side, fit them together as best you can. Since these bones probably came from different cats, they will not fit ideally. Examine and compare with mounted cat and human skeletons if available.

The bones of the anterior and posterior limbs of cat and man are considered as being **homologous,** since they are similar in origin and structure. They are **endochondral,** or performed in cartilage, and the number of bones in comparable regions are almost the same. Sometimes there are extra toes on the forelimb of the cat, making a total of seven. The presence of extra toes is considered an **atavistic character.**

SPINAL COLUMN (CERVICAL, THORACIC, LUMBAR, SACRAL, AND COCCYGEAL VERTEBRAE)

The spinal column consists of a chain of somewhat similar bones called vertebrae. They are developed on the same general plan, but different degrees of ossification and variations in function have been important factors in causing them to appear differently in the highly specialized vertebrates, as in cat and man. There are five principal regions or groups in the cat's spinal column. Representative vertebrae from each of these groups will now be considered.

CERVICAL VERTEBRAE (Fig. 12)

1. The **atlas,** or **first cervical vertebra,** is distinctive in having large, flat **transverse processes,** a very small or no **neural spine,**

and in not having a centrum. It has a large **vertebral canal**, through which the spinal cord passes to join the medulla oblongata within the skull. The **vertebral canal** is bounded on the sides and above by the **neural arch**, the dorsal portion of which may be determined by having more bony material. The **transverse processes** are winglike, with a small **transverse foramen** passing through the posterior part of each. The neural arch spreads at its anterior end to pass laterally to each occipital condyle of the skull, thus serving as **articulating surfaces**, or **facets**. Fit the atlas onto the skull in order to see the relationships. These parts may not fit together well since they probably came from different cats. Immediately posterior and dorsal to each of the anterior articulating surfaces is a small opening, the **cervical foramen**, for the passage of the first cervical nerve. Pass a small wire through each of the foramina of this vertebra in order to better determine the extent of each. The **posterior articulating facets** are on the inner walls of the vertebral canal.

2. The **axis**, or **second cervical vertebra** (Fig. 13), is distinguished by having a long, narrow, anterior projection, the **dens**, or **odontoid process**, and an enlarged, laterally compressed **neural spine**. The odontoid process consists of most of the centrum of the first vertebra, which is fused with the centrum of the second, forming a toothlike projection. This process forms the axis

around which the first vertebra turns when the head is rotated from side to side. The laterally compressed neural spine furnishes a large area for the attachment of muscles. A short **transverse process** surrounds a small **transverse foramen** on each side of the posterior portion of the **centrum**. The **anterior articulating surfaces**, or **facets**, are large, oval, smooth areas near the base of the odontoid process. For the most part the facets face laterally and only slightly upward. The **posterior articulating processes**, or zygapophyses, have facets that face downward. The anterior and posterior ends of a vertebra may be determined by the way these facets face; however, articulating facets do not develop on all vertebrae. Fit the atlas onto the axis and the axis onto the skull; observe that when the skull is rotated, there is a greater movement between these vertebrae than between the atlas and the skull.

If possible, observe these structures on the human skeleton.

3. A **typical cervical vertebra** (Fig. 14) is described as follows. The third, fourth, fifth, or sixth vertebra is typical. There are **seven cervical vertebrae** in most mammals. A cat, elephant, giraffe, and man have the same number. The first two vertebrae (atlas and axis) are much the same in these animals as those described earlier. The most distinctive structural characteristic that is found on the majority of cervical vertebrae is the small **transverse foramen** within the

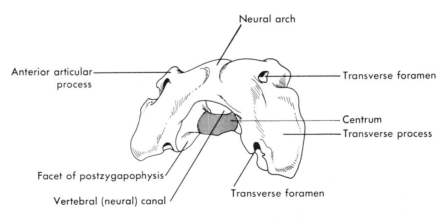

Anterior articular process

Neural arch

Transverse foramen

Centrum

Transverse process

Facet of postzygapophysis

Vertebral (neural) canal

Transverse foramen

Fig. 12. Atlas vertebra, caudodorsal view.

19

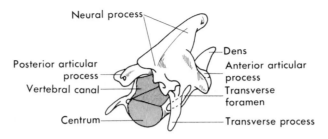

Fig. 13. Axis vertebra, caudo-right lateral view.

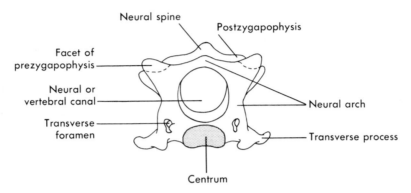

Fig. 14. Typical cervical vertebra, cephalic view.

base of the transverse process on each side of the **centrum, or body;** however, the seventh cervical vertebra of the cat does not usually have this foramen because the **vestigial rib** that completes the foramen is not fused with the transverse processes. In other words there is a **remnant of a rib** on each of the first six cervical vertebrae in all mammals that completes the **transverse foramen** and projects as an extension of the **transverse process.** The **neural arch** surrounds the **vertebral canal** dorsal to the centrum, and projecting from its dorsal surface is the **neural spine,** or **process,** which varies in size and length in different vertebrae. The **neural arch** surrounds the **spinal cord,** and within it is the **neural canal.** The centra of adjacent vertebrae are typically separated from one another by an intervertebral disk. In addition to this disk there are usually specialized areas of contact where parts rub against one another. These areas of contact are called **articular facets.**

It is necessary to be able to determine the anterior and posterior extremities of vertebrae. This can be done by studying the **articular facets.** Examine a typical cer-vical vertebra. Hold it with the neural spine upward. The anterior articulating surfaces, or facets, that you see **face upward and slightly to the center.** The two projections that bear these facets are the **prezygapophyses,** likewise on the opposite extremity are the **postzygapophyses,** with facets that usually **face downward and slightly laterally.** Fit adjacent vertebrae together or examine a mounted skeleton and see how the facets rub against one another. The anterior articulating facets are usually further apart than are the posterior.

THORACIC VERTEBRAE AND RIBS
(Figs. 1 and 15)

The general structural characteristics of a typical thoracic vertebra include articulating surfaces or facets (as in the cervical), facets for the ribs, and **long neural spines,** which usually **project posteriorward.** By this posteriorward projection the spines better brace themselves against the pull of the muscles that hold up the head. The neural spines of the last four thoracic vertebrae project forward, since their principal muscles extend back to the pelvic region

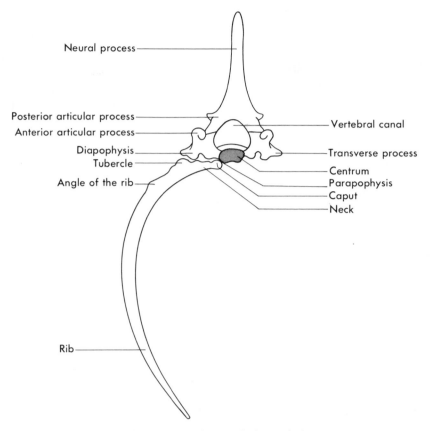

Neural process

Posterior articular process
Anterior articular process
Diapophysis
Tubercle
Angle of the rib

Vertebral canal

Transverse process
Centrum
Parapophysis
Caput
Neck

Rib

Fig. 15. Thoracic vertebra and rib, cephalic view.

and the pull on the spines is in the opposite direction from the thoracic. This is better seen on the mounted skeleton of the cat. These spines project posteriorward in man also, and although man carries his body in an erect position, this suggests that his ancestors may have carried their bodies in a horizontal position. The prezygapophyses and postzygapophyses with facets are present as they are in the cervical vertebrae. Each thoracic vertebra has two short articulating transverse processes on each side. The upper, or **diapophysis**, projects laterally from the neural arch, whereas the lower one, the base of the **parapophysis**, is reduced to an articulating surface on the side of the centrum. In fact, parts of two articulating surfaces may often be seen on one side of the centrum, because the head of the rib joins the vertebra in such a manner as to touch two vertebrae. Each half of an articulating surface on the centrum is a demifacet. Compare a thoracic vertebra

with a cervical vertebra, which was examined previously, for homologous structures.

The proximal end of the thoracic rib bears a close relationship to the lateral articulating surface of the thoracic vertebrae just mentioned. At the extreme upper end of the rib is an articulating surface known as the **head**, or **caput**, which joins with the **parapophysis** of the centrum. A small projection on the rib close to the caput is the **tubercle**, and this likewise joins or articulates with the **diapophysis** of the vertebra. The **neck** of the rib is the constriction between the caput and the tubercle.

Fit the caput and tubercle of the rib against the parapophysis and diapophysis, respectively. The space formed between these four parts is homologous with the transverse foramen of a cervical vertebra. Hence, the part that completes the transverse foramen in the neck vertebrae is really the proximal end of a rib. On the lateral

21

surface of a typical rib is a projection called the **angle of rib.** This is not present on all the ribs of all cats. The rib continues ventralward, and the **shaft** joins what is usually a rather long costal cartilage that is intermediate between the rib proper and the sternum. In different cats this cartilage may be found in various degrees of ossification.

LUMBAR VERTEBRAE (Fig. 16)

The lumbar vertebrae are distinctive in having large, long **transverse processes** that project in an **anterolateral** direction. This is probably the result of their response to the pull of the more important muscles attached to them. These muscles extend to the pelvic girdle and to the posterior limbs. The smooth, cup-shaped articulating surfaces, or facets, of the **prezygapophyses** face toward the center and upward, whereas the articulating surfaces of the **postzygapophyses** face outward and downward. Below these on each side is often an **accessory articulating process** that helps to lock these vertebrae more firmly together and thus makes the back stronger. The lumbar vertebrae are relatively large, especially the **centrum.** The heavy but short **neural spine** projects anteriorward, and the **vertebral canal** is large.

The first lumbar vertebra of man sometimes has a **vestigial rib.** This rib is normal in the gorilla, hence it is known as the "gorilla rib" when it occurs in man. It is considered an "anomaly."

SACRAL VERTEBRAE (Fig. 17)

The **sacrum,** or synsacrum, consists of three vertebrae fused into one bone; however, the outline of each vertebra is easily seen on the ventral surface. Two pairs of **dorsal intervertebral foramina** and two pairs of **ventral intervertebral foramina** are present, the size of each depending on the extent of ossification or fusion of transverse processes. These foramina represent the spaces between transverse processes of vertebrae (see Figs. 41 and 72). These foramina serve for the passage of afferent and efferent roots of sacral nerves, respectively. The anteromedian processes are the **prezygapophyses** with small, smooth **articular facets,** and the large, winglike projections

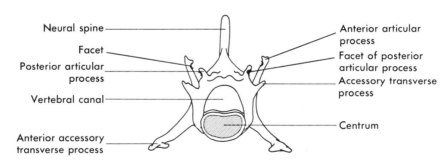

Fig. 16. Lumbar vertebra, caudal view.

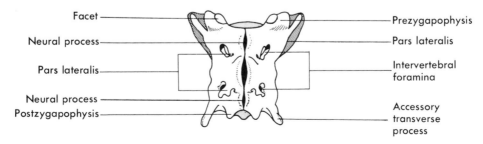

Fig. 17. Sacrum, or three sacral vertebrae, dorsal view.

are **transverse processes,** or **partes laterales.** Partes laterales, because of the evidence shown in their embryological development, are believed to be remains, or **vestiges,** of ribs, which articulate with the ilium. At the posterior extremity of the sacrum, the projections near the vertebral canal are the **postzygapophyses** with articulating facets. Three **neural spines** extend dorsally, and laterally to these on each side there is a a row of four **tubercles** that converge posteriorly. These are **fused prearticular** and **postarticular processes,** or **zygapophyses.** Cartilage separates the **pars lateralis** from each **ilium,** and this relaxes in the female when she gives birth to the young, or parturition. According to H. H. Wilder,* "the sacral region of man consists normally of the fusion of five vertebrae, but there are records of seven, which should serve to dispel the idea that the body of man (or any other animal) is formed in accordance with

---

*Wilder, H. H.: History of the human body, New York, 1923, Henry Holt & Company, p. 131.

a definite pattern, or is constructed on any other principle, save those of heredity and environment."

COCCYGEAL, OR CAUDAL, VERTEBRAE (Figs. 18 and 19)

The coccygeal, or caudal, vertebrae are very different in structure from the base to the tip of the tail. This variation depends on the extent of ossification of the various vertebrae.

Fig. 18 shows a vertebra close to the base of the tail. The **first ten vertebrae** in this region are **most nearly typical** for the entire spinal column, since most of the major parts found in any vertebra are present. The neural arch and the **anterior and posterior zygapophyses,** with their articulating surfaces and short neural spines, are well formed. The **transverse processes** are unusually well developed for the size of the vertebrae, and on the ventroanterior ends of the centra are what are interpreted as being remnants of the **hemal arches,** known as **chevron bones.** There may be several

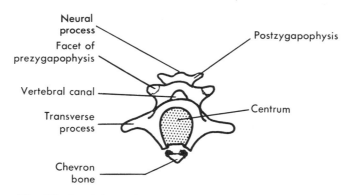

Fig. 18. Caudal vertebra near base of tail, cephalic view.

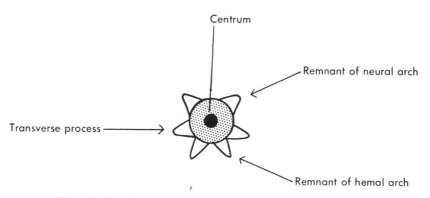

Fig. 19. Caudal vertebra near end of tail, cephalic view.

of these, beginning with the **fifth vertebra**. No other vertebrae of the cat have hemal arch remnants, and it is especially because of these remnants, in addition to the other structures of the vertebrae, that the first eight or ten caudal vertebrae are considered **most nearly typical** of all of the vertebrae of the cat's spinal column. Fig. 19 shows a vertebra of the caudal portion of the tail, where the centrum is almost all that remains of the vertebra; however, remnants of the bases of the **neural** and **hemal arches** are present. The bases of the former are farther apart and longer. The parts of the **transverse processes** are also present. When one eats canned salmon, he often finds partially calcified vertebrae in which the centra is about all that is left. In man there are remnants of only three to five centra remaining of the caudal vertebrae.

When one looks at the spinal column of the cat from the side, as in Fig. 1, he observes a long arch, but when one looks at the spinal column of man in an erect position and from the right side, he sees the spinal column in a form somewhat like the capital letter **S**, which serves like a spring in supporting the body. As man becomes older this shape tends to change and becomes somewhat like the capital letter **C**, as in a stooped old person. Examine the mounted skeletons of cat and man. The arched spinal column of a quadruped mammal is indicative of a strong back and is a desirable, favorable point in grading and judging farm animals at the International Livestock Show in Chicago each year.

SOME DIFFERENCES IN VERTEBRAL, OR SPINAL, COLUMNS OF CAT AND MAN

1. Variations in the number of vertebrae:

Regions	Cat	Man
Cervical	7	7
Thoracic	13	12
Lumbar	7	5
Sacral	3	5
Caudal, or coccygeal	4-26	3-5

2. Thoracic vertebrae in the cat have relatively longer and larger neural spines or processes than in man.

3. Transverse processes on lumbar vertebrae are relatively longer and project toward the skull at a more acute angle in the cat than in man.

4. Vestigial chevron bones occasionally project ventrally from the anterior ends of the fifth to the thirteenth coccygeal vertebrae in the cat. These are absent in man.

5. The first eight or ten coccygeal vertebrae are much nearer being typical than any others of the cat. The few coccygeal vertebrae present in man are vestigial and are mere remnants of typical vertebrae.

6. Man has twelve pairs of ribs; the cat has thirteen.

7. Man has seven pairs of true ribs; the cat has nine. True ribs are attached separately to the sternum.

8. Man has five pairs of false ribs; the cat has four. False ribs are not attached directly to the sternum.

9. Man has two pairs of floating ribs; the cat has one pair. Floating ribs are those that are not attached at their ventral ends.

10. The body of the sternum in man is fused into one piece, but there are four sternebrae in the embryo. In the cat the body consists of six sternebrae that are movably united.

11. The metacromian process of the cat scapula is absent, as such, in man.

12. Normally five vertebrae fuse to form the sacrum of man; three vertebrae fuse in the cat.

13. In the cat there are seven lumbar vertebrae but only five in man.

REVIEW QUESTIONS ON SPINAL COLUMN

1. What are the parts of a typical cervical vertebra? (Fig. 14)

2. Which of all the vertebrae of the cat are most nearly typical? (Fig. 18)

3. What are the principal distinctive, structural characteristics of the vertebrae in each of the five regions in the spinal column of a cat? (Figs. 14 to 19)

4. What are the structural differences between the first two vertebrae of the neck and the other cervical vertebrae? (Figs. 12 to 19)

5. What are some of the factors that probably help to determine the direction in which neural spines and transverse processes project? (Fig. 1)

6. How do the vertebrae of the sacrum differ in a cat and man? (Figs. 2 and 17)

7. Which vertebrae of the cat have the longest neural spines or processes? Why?

8. What general statements may be made concerning the differences in the caudal, or coccygeal, vertebrae of the cat? (Figs. 18 and 19)

9. What parts of the spinal column or vertebrae do we often find when eating canned salmon?

10. How may the anterior or the posterior end of a vertebra be determined by studying the articulating surfaces?

11. How does the number of vertebrae vary in the cat and in man?

12. Which vertebra has no centrum? (See mounted skeletons, Fig. 12)

13. Would you say that the vertebrae of the cat and man, in comparable regions, are quite similar in structure? (Observe mounted skeletons.)

14. Are all vertebrae of cat and man built on the same general plan? (Compare mounted skeletons of each.)

15. Are the anterior or the posterior limbs and girdles of the cat more firmly attached (normally) to the spinal column? (Observe the mounted skeleton.)

16. What is the advantage or disadvantage of loose or more firm attachment of the cat's limbs to the body? (Observe the mounted skeleton.)

17. Briefly, how do the long bones of the leg increase in length?

18. Does the cat or man come more nearly walking and running on his toes? Explain. (Rely on your own observation for the answer.)

PELVIC GIRDLE (Fig. 20)

Each half of the pelvic girdle is called an innominate bone and consists embryonically of three separate parts: the anterior, or **ilium**; the posterodorsal, or **ischium**; and the posteroventral, or **pubis**. In a young mammal the lines of the unions of these three parts may be seen easily. The **crest of the ilium** is at its anterior extremity, and the **tuberosity of the ischium** is at its posterior end. The **acetabulum** is the cup for the articulation of the femur. The large space separating the pubis and ischium is the **obturator foramen**. On the dorsal surface of the innominate bone, close to the acetabulum, is the **spine of the ischium**. Anterior to this spine is the **greater sciatic notch**, over which passes the great sciatic nerve. Posterior to this spine is the **lesser sciatic notch**, over which passes the **lesser sciatic** or **cutaneous femoris posterior nerve**. The **pubic symphysis** is the median line of fusion of the two innominate bones.

The **pelvis** consists of the two **innominate bones**, the **sacrum**, and the **coccyx**. It is perhaps the weakest part of the entire human skeleton. Its greatest test in the female human comes at the time of childbirth. To avoid this crucial test and the uncertainties involved, **cesarean operations** are often performed.

The ilium joins the sacrum, which gives a firm connection of the hind legs with the spinal column; this enables quick locomotion of the whole body, particularly in quadrupeds. The **pectoral girdle**, however, is attached to the body or its bones only by muscles. The muscles act as a spring or shock absorber when landing first on the front legs following a jump. The bend of the limb at the joints helps also.

FEMUR (Fig 21)

The proximal end of the femur has a pronounced, rounded **head** that fits into the acetabulum of the pelvic girdle. Near the center of the head is a depression, the **fovea capitis**. The constriction adjacent to the head is the **neck**. The larger tuberosity at the proximal end is the **great trochanter**, whereas the pronounced depression, when viewed from the posterior surface, is the **trochanteric fossa**. The **lesser trochanter** is immediately below this fossa. The rough line distal to the lesser trochanter and extending diagonally is the **linea aspera**. The distal extremity is marked by the **lateral condyle** and the **median condyle**, which are separated by **intercondyloid fossa**. There is a small **lateral epicondyle** adjacent to the lateral condyle. The right and left femurs may be determined by the fact that the head of the femur is on the median side and the posterior surface of the femur is slightly concave; in addition the condyles at the distal end project posteriorly.

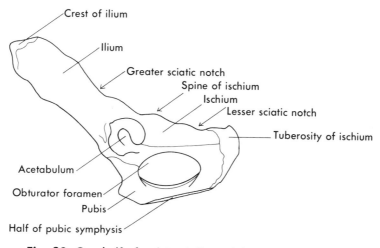

Crest of ilium

Ilium

Greater sciatic notch

Spine of ischium

Ischium

Lesser sciatic notch

Tuberosity of ischium

Acetabulum

Obturator foramen

Pubis

Half of pubic symphysis

Fig. 20. One-half of pelvic girdle or left innominate bone.

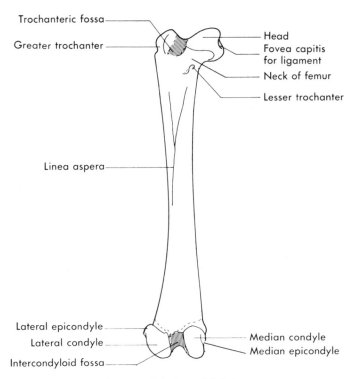

Fig. 21. Caudal view of left femur.

Trochanteric fossa

Greater trochanter

Head

Fovea capitis for ligament

Neck of femur

Lesser trochanter

Linea aspera

Lateral epicondyle

Lateral condyle

Intercondyloid fossa

Median condyle

Median epicondyle

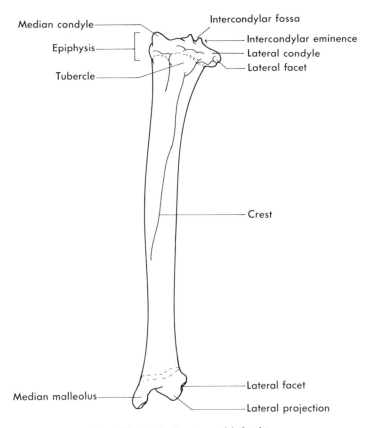

Fig. 22. Cephalic view of left tibia.

Median condyle

Epiphysis

Tubercle

Intercondylar fossa

Intercondylar eminence

Lateral condyle

Lateral facet

Crest

Median malleolus

Lateral facet

Lateral projection

TIBIA, OR SHINBONE (Fig. 22)

At the proximal end of the tibia the **epiphysis** is quite large and is easily seen. It separates off easily when bones of a young cat are boiled in cleaning. It consists of a **lateral condyle** on the more concave side and has a **facet** for the articulation of the fibula. The **median condyle** is opposite the external condyle and is slightly higher. Between the two articulating surfaces for the femur is an **intercondylar projection** that contains an **intercondylar fossa**. A small, blunt **tubercle** is on the cephalic edge below the epiphysis for the articulation of the patella. Below this is the crest of the tibia, or shinbone, which extends downward and gradually decreases as the shaft becomes more nearly cylindrical. The distal end has an irregular depressed articulating surface, the inner wall of which forms a projection, the **median malleolus**. A lateral projection has a **facet** at its base for articulation with the fibula.

From the foregoing description determine whether you have a right or a left tibia.

FIBULA (Fig. 23)

The fibula is well ossified only on older specimens. Hence the **epiphyseal** ends come off easily on young cats. You should have a well-ossified fibula in order to identify the following parts: On the median surface of the proximal end, or **head**, is a **facet** for the articulation with the lateral condyle of the tibia. The **shaft**, or **diaphysis**, is long, irregular, and slender. The distal end has a pronounced groove for the passage of the tendon of the peroneus longus muscle. A projection on the outer boundary of the groove is the **lateral malleolus**. On the median surface of the distal end of the fibula is a large articulating surface for the calcaneus, or heel bone, and above it is a smaller trianguler facet for the tibia.

From the foregoing description determine whether you have the right or the left fibula. Fit the femur, tibia, and fibula together properly. This can be done only if they all belong to the right side or all to the left side. See a mounted skeleton if it is available.

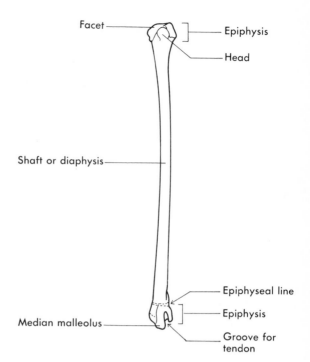

Fig. 23. Lateral view of left fibula.

GROWTH OF LONG BONES

Each of the three **endochondral** long bones of each leg has an **epiphysis** at each end, separated from a longer shaft, or **diaphysis**, by a **cartilaginous area**. Because of this cartilage the epiphyses, or ends, of the long leg bones of a young animal come off easily, especially when boiled in cleaning. It is on the **shaft side of this cartilage area** where the **greatest cell division** or **growth** takes place. This growth adds to the length of the **shaft**, or **diaphysis**, by **pushing the epiphysis away**, thus adding to the length of the entire bone. This is how the legs elongate and the height of the animal increases. Cartilage **does not** turn into bone but is absorbed and replaced by osteogenic cells brought in by blood vessels, which produce the bone. This, quite briefly, is how **endochondral**, or **cartilaginous, bones** grow. The **membranous**, or **dermal, bones** of the skull form directly from connective tissue and do not pass through a cartilaginous stage.

SOME DIFFERENCES IN SKELETONS OF CAT AND MAN

As you read the following summary, refer to mounted skeletons of cat and man, if available, in order to better see their similarities and differences.

1. Man has 126 bones, whereas the cat usually has 116 to 148. There is much variation in the tail of the cat.

2. The clavicle of the cat is relatively smaller and is not in contact with the manubrium nor the scapula, as in man, but is embedded in muscle.

3. A supracondyloid foramen is present on the humerus of the cat but is absent in man.

4. The pubic symphysis is better ossified in the cat than it is in man.

5. The cat has seven carpal bones, whereas man has eight.

6. Man has five fingers and five toes normally. Occasionally there is a reduction in the number of fingers. However, there are records of the human baby having six toes on each foot. The cat has five in front and only four on each hind foot. Occasionally the cat has six toes on each front foot.

7. Claws are on the ends of the toes of the cat, whereas nails are on the ends of the toes of man. However, claws are retractable.

8. The cat walks with only the digits touching the ground and therefore is a digitigrade, whereas man walks with his digits, sole of the foot, and heel touching the ground and therefore is a plantigrade.

9. The cat's spinal column is carried in an arched or a nearly horizontal position, whereas that of man is almost vertical. The nearly horizontal position, as in the cat, is better for the most efficient functioning of the internal organs, particularly the digestive, urogenital, and circulatory systems.

10. The vertebrae of the cat are much more varied in structure in different regions than those in man. The long neural processes of the thoracic region are for the attachment of muscles that support the head on a nearly horizontal neck. The caudal vertebrae of the cat are much more numerous, whereas in man they are reduced to three or four.

11. The shapes of the skulls in man and cat are quite different, largely because of the great enlargement of the cerebrum in man that pushed the frontal and parietal bones dorsally and the nose ventrally or anteriorly.

12. On the ventral surface of a few of the caudal vertebrae of the cat are chevron bones, interpreted as being remnants of hemal arches.

13. The transverse processes of the lumbar vertebrae of the cat project sharply forward for the attachment of muscles extending posteriorly to the pelvic girdle. This condition is more pronounced in animals that climb trees.

14. In the cat the length of the femur is correlated with the space between the acetabulum and the last rib, so that when a cat jumps, the distal end of the femur will not hit the rib. Man does not bring the knee as close to the ribs, and the space is not equal to the length of the femur.

15. A kitten is able to walk in a few days after birth, a calf in a few hours, but a human child is usually about one year old before he is able to walk; yet we humans think we are so smart. It is much easier to balance on four legs rather than two. Compare (Figs. 1 and 2) particularly the way the hind feet come in contact with the ground. The same mechanical principle is involved in a four-wheeled wagon and a two-wheeled cart. The flat foot of man helps to compensate for the lack of four feet. The erect position of man requires a stronger sacrum and is much more unstable and difficult to maintain on two legs than the horizontal position of the body with four legs for support. When man first learns to locomote, he goes on his hands and knees, which is equivalent to four legs.

REVIEW QUESTIONS ON PELVIC AND LIMB BONES

1. What are the basic or fundamental parts of the pectoral girdle of cat or man?

2. Which of the cat's girdles is more firmly attached to the spinal column and what is the advantage of each type?

3. Name the parts that surround the transverse foramen of a typical cervical vertebra. (Figs. 14 and 15)

4. What are the advantages of having two legs or four legs?

5. State some of the advantages and some of the disadvantages of the erect position of the body of man.

6. Which performs the greater function, the clavicle of a cat or of man? (To answer, use your own judgment. Consider the movements of the forelimbs.)

7. Are limb bones endochondral or membranous?

8. How many vertebrae are a part of the sacrum in the cat? How many in man? Does the erect position demand more vertebrae?

9. Name ten structural differences in the skeleton of a cat and man.

10. What facts of the anterior and posterior limb bones in cat and man indicate that they are homologous? (Figs. 1 and 2)

11. Which bones of the skull are membranous and which are endochondral in origin?

12. How do the number of vertebrae vary in cat and man?

13. What are the remnants of the hemal arches, as found in the cat, called? (Fig. 18)

14. What bones merge to form the innominate? (Fig. 20)

15. How are the claws of a cat arranged so that they may be used effectively or not used on an instant's notice? (Examine a live cat.)

16. What is the condition and apparent function of the coracoid process in the bird, cat, and man?

17. Give an example for each of the three functions of bones.

18. Name two bones from different groups that function in all three ways.

19. Which limb bones of the cat may be considered as homologous with those of man? (Figs. 3 and 5)

20. What are chevron bones, and where are they found?

2

Muscles of the cat

INTRODUCTION

The dissection of the cat is one of the best ways to prepare for the dissection of the human body, which is required in the first year of all medical and dental schools. The dissection of the cat is strongly recommended for nurses and physical education students, because after careful dissection one remembers by visualization, which is the best known way to learn anatomy. In doing this work it is best for the student to read, previous to each laboratory period, the information that will be covered.

Most cats prepared for dissection have not had the skin removed. This may be done in different ways, but the author prefers the following method. Cut through the skin down the center of the back, from the base of the tail to the top of the head, and dissect it away from the left side by cutting the loose connective tissue or fascia. On the side of the head and neck the fine fibers of the **platysma muscle** will be cut and some will come off with the skin, but most fibers remain on the neck (see Fig. 24). Make a transverse cut of the skin from the top of the shoulder blades or scapulae, down on the lateral surface of the left front leg. Cut the skin and the ear off close to the skull in back of the eyes and the corner of the mouth. As the skin is being removed from the side of the leg and shoulder, the dark **brachiocephalic,** or **cephalic humeral vein** should be seen. Make another cut of the skin down the side of the left hind leg.

Dissect off the skin from the left side of the body to the midventral line or **raphe.**

If the cat was **pregnant** or **nursing** kittens, the **mammary** or **milk glands** can be seen along the ventral surface between the skin and underlying muscles. There are usually four or five pairs of nipples and mammary glands. The anterior mammary glands are supplied by the **mammary artery,** which in the female extends below the diaphragm and is called the **superior epigastric artery.** The posterior mammary glands are supplied by the **inferior epigastric artery** (see Figs. 57 and 58). The inferior epigastric is cut in the groin when skinning the cat and is usually injected red.

In the elephant, bat, monkey, and man the mammary glands are usually confined to the **pectoral region,** but in the horse, cow, sheep, and goat these glands are in the **inguinal region;** however, in the dog, cat, pig, and rat they are all along the ventral surface. Occasionally in man there are cases in which five or more irregular pairs of nipples occur.

You may remove the entire skin in one piece if you like and use it later to wrap around the specimen to help keep it from drying, or you may discard the skin. Ask your laboratory instructor which he prefers.

If your cat happens to be a male, carefully dissect off the skin from around the testes, penis, and sperm ducts, leaving them uninjured (Fig. 51). If the cat has been properly injected and embalmed, there is

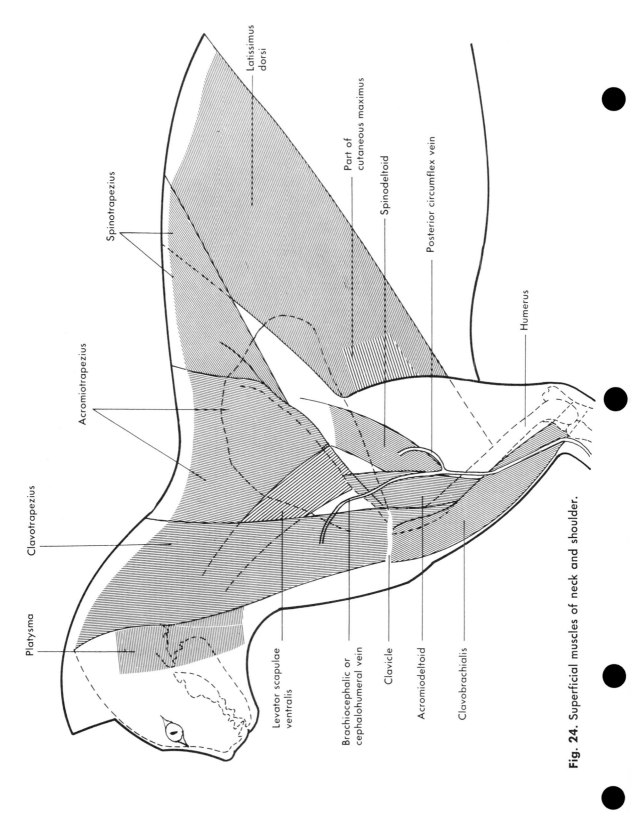

Fig. 24. Superficial muscles of neck and shoulder.

Latissimus dorsi

Part of cutaneous maximus

Spinodeltoid

Posterior circumflex vein

Humerus

Spinotrapezius

Acromiotrapezius

Clavotrapezius

Platysma

Levator scapulae ventralis

Brachiocephalic or cephalohumeral vein

Clavicle

Acromiodeltoid

Clavobrachialis

34

little danger that it will become unfit for dissecting because of decomposition. If there are signs that decomposition has begun, the specimen should be immersed in a 6 to 8 percent formalin solution. If the specimen is to be worked on over a period of several weeks, there is some danger of it drying too much. If you wish to avoid using formalin, wrap the specimen in wet newspaper and tie it up securely.

Also, the specimen may be placed in a plastic bag to prevent drying. If a plastic bag is used, it is best to clip or chop off the claws. The author advises chopping off the feet below the wrist or ankle with a hatchet.

Myology is the science that treats of the form, location, and attachments of muscles. The end of the muscle nearer the median plane of the body or farther up on the limb is known as its **origin,** whereas the place of attachment to the bone that it moves is known as its **insertion.** Usually skeletal muscles arise and terminate in white fibrous tissues known as tendons. The skeletal muscles are usually named according to their function, shape, or parts to which they are attached. Muscles are covered by **fascia,** called **epimysium,** which also binds them together and which must be broken in order to separate the muscles. **Deep fascia** lies close against the muscles and dips down between them. **Loose fascia** lies under the skin and holds it to the muscles. Tendons, ligaments, and aponeuroses are forms of heavy fascia, and each is a form of connective tissue.

The **aponeuroses** and flat, white tendons are the stronger portions of this fascia. A **raphe** consists of the ridge or furrow along the line of union of halves of symmetrical parts, as down the middle of the back or of the chest or abdomen. The **raphe** indicates the position of the median vertical plane of bilateral symmetry.

Dissection consists of **intelligent separation** of one structure from another and the **reflection** of known parts in order to study those lying deeper in the specimen. When reflecting a muscle, cut it into two parts transversely, turn each part back to expose deeper organs, but always retain the **origin**

and **insertion** of each muscle studied. "Bisect" means to cut transversely into two parts. This cut is usually made near the center or middle of the muscle.

The **skeletal muscles** arise from myotomes, or myomeres, of the mesoblastic, or mesodermal, embryonic sections of mesoderm. Muscles are combinations of these somites, or myotomes, which are seen in various stages of fusion. Few muscles arise from a single somite. Basically, a pair of spinal nerves supplies each pair of somites. The **intercostal muscles** represent individual somites, but these are split horizontally into the external and the internal. Most muscles in the cat and in man are formed by merging, or fusion, of several somites, and each, with few exceptions, retains its **original nerve;** however, these nerves merge with one another and may again separate, which complicates identification.

Histologically, there are **three kinds of muscles.**

1. **Skeletal** muscle, which is **striated,** constitutes the flesh of an animal and is under the control of the will. Skeletal muscles are the most numerous and produce most of the movements. There are four different groups of skeletal muscles, depending on their location, as discussed in the following section.

2. **Cardiac muscle,** which is **striated,** constitutes the heart and is involuntary.

3. **Smooth muscle,** which is **nonstriated,** is located in the walls of the blood vessels and digestive tract.

FOUR MAJOR GROUPS OF SKELETAL MUSCLES

1. **Integumentary,** or **skin, muscles** are attached to the underside of the skin and are mostly removed with the skin.

2. **Appendicular muscles** constitute the meat or flesh on the girdle and limb bones and are perhaps the most outstanding of the four major groups.

3. **Axial muscles** lie along the spinal column and are attached largely to the bones or vertebrae of the spinal column.

4. **Branchial muscles** were originally between the cartilages or bones of the gill

arches and were used to move the gills and hence, indirectly, were used in respiration; in cat and man they lie between the bones and cartilages that constitute the lower jaws, larynx, and manubrium.

The following groups of muscles are arranged for convenience in dissection and study. The majority of them are appendicular in that they are associated with the girdles and limbs, but the other three major groups are also represented.

The description of each muscle is general, and the student is left to work out the details. There is a considerable variation in muscles, so do not expect the descriptions to be accurate in all details. Begin the dissection of the muscles on the left side of the cat. Turn the specimen onto its right side with its head to your left and the feet directed toward you.

INTEGUMENTARY, OR SKIN, MUSCLES (Fig. 24)

Most skin muscles are removed with the skin, but parts remain on your specimen. Identify these remnants on the left side of the cat and loosen their edges. They are very thin and appear as fine lines.

1. The **cutaneous maximus muscle** is thin and covers most of the side of the body. It lies between the skin and the muscles of the body wall and is usually dissected off with the skin. Identify this muscle and determine the direction in which its fibers extend in different regions. It becomes thicker in the lateral wall of the chest where it fuses with the latissimus dorsi in the axillary region. If the skin has been removed, portions of the cutaneous maximus may be found closely attached to the latissimus dorsi ventral to the scapula. This extremity is considered as its origin, and the insertion is on the underside of a large area of the skin. The cutaneous maximus muscle causes much of the hair to stand on end when the cat becomes frightened; it is not found in man.

2. The **platysma** lies on the lateral side of the neck and head; some fibers may extend to the angle of the mouth. Many of these fibers are removed with the skin, but some may be seen covering the anterior end

of the large, blue-colored external jugular vein of the neck. This muscle moves the skin of the lateral region of the neck and face; it is much the same in man.

LEFT LATERAL VIEW OF SUPERFICIAL MUSCLES OF NECK AND SHOULDER (Fig. 24)

Place the cat before you with its head to your left and its feet toward you.

Get the left scapula and humerus from your set of bones and check the names of their parts that are labeled in the drawing before you begin your study of the muscles. Place these two bones in their relative positions on your cat. Look at the clavicle on the mounted skeleton; this will refresh your mind as to the relative positions of these parts.

Begin the dissection of the following muscles on the left side of your cat. In this manual, when reference is made to the "**right or the left side**," it always means to the **right or the left side of the cat** and does not mean to your right or left as you look at the illustration. Think of your own body as being in the same position as that of the cat and you can determine accurately which is its right or left side. Remember that all drawings were made from large, well-developed cats. If you have a small specimen, you will have more difficulties. Dissect each muscle so it can be demonstrated to the instructor or to anyone else.

1. The **clavotrapezius** can be identified as follows. The **brachiocephalic vein** appears as a dark streak passing over the shoulder and turns deeply into the base of the neck (Fig. 24). This vein will not show if the blood has been drained out. Begin at the place where this vein turns into the neck and separate or loosen the posterior edge of the clavotrapezius muscle dorsal to and covering the vein above the shoulder. Insert a probe under the posterior edge of this muscle and toward the lower jaw. Find the anterior edge of the muscle and loosen its sides from the head to the clavicle and from the underlying muscles. The lower anterior edge of the muscle covers part of the large external jugular vein, previously seen, and inserts on or is attached to the

small clavicle. Many muscle fibers pass over the clavicle and continue down the foreleg, where they form the clavobrachialis muscle. The origin of the clavotrapezius is on the lambdoid crest of the skull and the first few cervical vertebrae. The dorsal half of the posterior edge of this muscle close to the vertebrae is continuous with or fused with the acromiotrapezius muscle immediately posterior to it. Separate these two muscles with scissors to the middorsal line. The lower portions of these muscles are separated by the **levator scapula ventralis,** most of which lies median to the clavotrapezius. Bisect, or cut in half, the clavotrapezius muscle at right angles to the direction of its fibers and reflect the two ends. The clavotrapezius draws the clavicle forward and upward.

2. The **clavobrachialis** is a continuation of the clavotrapezius below the clavicle and down the anterior part of the brachium, or upper arm. At its lower end it merges with the pectoantibrachialis muscle of the chest. Its posterior edge is close to the brachiocephalic vein. Loosen along this edge, pull it up, and discover its anterior limit as it merges with the pectoantibrachialis along a white line. Separate along this line, bisect, and reflect. This muscle compares to one of three that represent the deltoid of man. The other two are the spinodeltoid and acromiodeltoid, which are discussed later in this group.

3. The **acromiotrapezius** covers the upper part of the scapula, and most of its anterior edge merges with the clavotrapezius. It arises from fascia along the middorsal line near the tips of the neural spines of the thoracic vertebrae, and it inserts on the spine of the scapula. Near its anterior lower edge the acromiotrapezius is joined by the **levator scapula ventralis,** which comes up from under the clavotrapezius to attach to the spine of the scapula. The muscle fibers of the acromiotrapezius have receded from the neural spines, leaving the muscular sheath that serves as a tendon. Bisect through the muscular portion slightly below the upper edge of the scapula. This muscle helps to hold the upper edges of the scapulae together.

4. The **spinotrapezius** is posterior to and continuous with the acromiotrapezius and originates from the tips of the neural spines of the posterior thoracic vertebrae. It inserts on the caudal portion of the spine of the scapula, and the fibers extend to the upper lateral edge of the scapula. In man these three trapezius muscles are merged into one large trapezius. The spinotrapezius forms the lower portion of the large trapezius, which pulls the scapula toward the spinal column and dorsalward. Loosen the lower posterior edge of the spinotrapezius of the cat, insert a probe under its entire width, and bisect at right angles to the muscle fibers. Be sure to reflect this muscle completely because it covers part of the following muscle.

5. The **latissimus dorsi** is large, with its upper anterior edge covered by the spinotrapezius. It arises in fascia and aponeurosis from the opposite side along the middorsal line of the posterior thoracic region and most of the lumbar region. It covers most of the lateral surface of the body and extends forward and downward below the scapula where a portion of the cutaneous maximus may be seen. The latissimus dorsi inserts on the humerus, but before doing so it merges with the following muscles: (a) the teres major from the ventral edge of the scapula, (b) the epitrochlean from the inner surface of the upper arm, and (c) the xiphihumeralis of the pectoralis group. Do not try to identify these muscles at this time. Loosen the lower and upper edges of the latissimus dorsi along its entire extent and insert a probe under the middle, bisect, and reflect. The spinal nerves appear as white threads coming to this muscle to its median surface. The number of these nerves indicates the number of myomeres that have merged to form the muscle. At the upper posterior limits this muscle becomes continuous with a thin sheath that serves as a tendon. Apparently the muscle fibers have receded to get away from the neural spines. This muscle is attached to the humerus and gives it much power in pulling it backward when the cat is running or climbing. The amount of the **cutaneous maximus** muscle that is left on

the lower part of the latissimus dorsi depends on the size of the muscle and the amount left on the skin when the skin was removed.

6. The **spinodeltoid** muscle is covered by thin fascia near the cephalic end and below the spine of the scapula. Dissect off this fascia but do not injure the brachiocephalic or circumflex veins. The spinodeltoid muscle is about one-half inch wide and is immediately ventral to the spine of the scapula. Its lower edge is almost lateral to the lower edge of the scapula. The origin of the spinodeltoid is in fascia. The lower end continues as a wide tendinous sheath that extends under the brachiocephalic vein and the next muscle to be considered and inserts on the humerus. It helps to bend and outwardly rotate the humerus. Insert a probe under it, bisect, and reflect.

7. The **acromiodeltoid** muscle is about the same size as the spinodeltoid. Sometimes it appears double as it originates from the glenoid border of the acromion process of the scapula and at times on the adjacent metacromion process. The greater part inserts on the tendon of the spinodeltoid, but the outer fibers continue to the humerus. The spinodeltoid and acromiodeltoid are homologous with a large, single deltoid in man. In both cat and man it flexes the humerus and rotates it outwardly. Bisect and reflect, separating it from underlying muscles.

The **brachiocephalic, or cephalic humeral, vein** gives off a branch below and posterior to the lower end of the spinodeltoid muscle. This is the **posterior circumflex,** which usually passes deeply below the spinodeltoid muscle to join the subclavian vein or the transverse scapular vein (see Fig. 52). The brachiocephalic usually continues up over the shoulder, turns inward between the clavotrapezius and levator scapula ventralis muscles, and joins the subscapular vein, which empties into the subclavian. Sometimes it does not turn in deeply and join the transverse scapular but continues across the outer surface of the clavotrapezius and joins the external jugular directly. Color the brachiocephalic vein blue.

Cats vary greatly in the completeness, or thoroughness, in which they are injected. Some blood vessels are well injected in some cats, whereas these same vessels are not injected in other specimens. If they are not injected, you probably cannot identify them. If you color each muscle in Fig. 24 red, it will make them more realistic and thus aid you in visualizing them.

LEFT LATERAL VIEW OF DEEPER MUSCLES OF NECK AND SHOULDER (Fig. 25)

In Fig. 25 the superficial muscles have been removed.

1. The **occipitoscapularis,** sometimes called the levator scapulae dorsalis (rhomboideus capitus), lies under the clavotrapezius on the upper lateral part of the neck. It is attached on the lambdoid crest and inserts on the upper edge of the scapula. It is less than a centimeter wide and lies close upon other neck muscles. In man this muscle is a part of the rhomboideus minor. Its action is to rotate and draw the scapula forward. Bisect and reflect.

2. The **splenius** is large and flat, covering most of the side of the neck close to the vertebrae and median to the occipitoscapularis. It is composed of many short muscles that are united into one mass, and it aids in raising the head. This muscle cannot be loosened or bisected with satisfaction.

3. The **rhomboideus minor,** median to the acromiotrapezius, is larger than the rhomboideus major in the cat and lies anterior to it. The origin is on the spinous process of the cervical and thoracic vertebrae and extends to the dorsal border of the scapula. The insertion is posterior to and in close contact with the insertion of the occipitoscapularis muscle. It draws the scapula dorsalward and forward. Pull the upper edge of the scapula away from the thoracic vertebrae about two inches and bisect carefully, leaving half attached to the scapula.

4. The **rhomboideus major** lies along the posterior edge of the rhomboideus minor, and their edges are often partly fused. It arises from the thoracic neural spines and inserts at the dorsoposterior angle of the scapula, where it becomes more distinct.

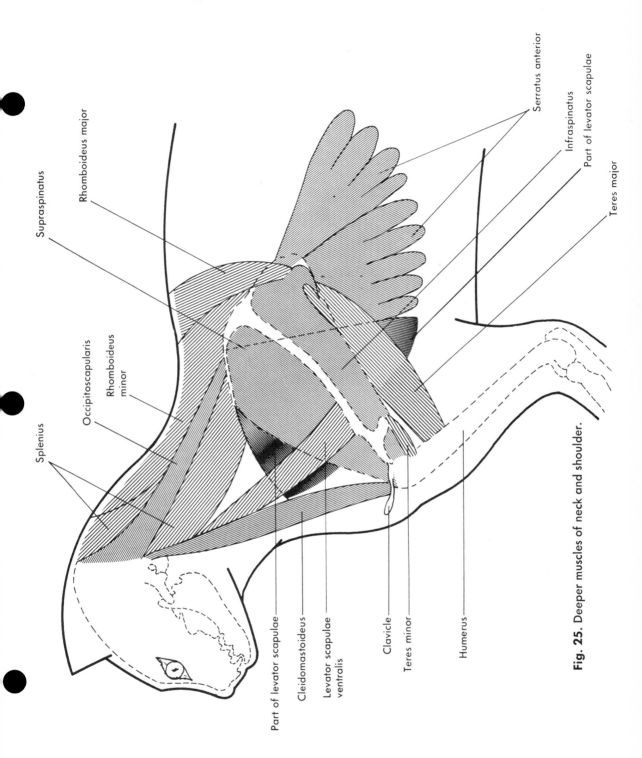

Supraspinatus

Rhomboideus major

Serratus anterior

Infraspinatus

Part of levator scapulae

Teres major

Occipitoscapularis

Rhomboideus minor

Splenius

Part of levator scapulae

Cleidomastoideus

Levator scapulae ventralis

Clavicle

Teres minor

Humerus

Fig. 25. Deeper muscles of neck and shoulder.

39

Bisect carefully, leaving half attached to the scapula. The **rhomboideus major** and **minor** seem to be incorrectly named on the cat, since the major is the smaller; however, they were first named on man, where **the major is the larger.**

5. The **levator scapula ventralis** arises from the transverse processes of the cervical vertebrae under the anterior end of the clavotrapezius and extends backward, where it joins the anterior edge of the acromiotrapezius, and the two muscles insert on the lower portion of the spine of the scapula. It draws the scapula forward. Bisect. See the mounted skeleton for the relationship of bones. This muscle is not found in man.

6. The **cleidomastoid** muscle lies below the lower edge of the clavotrapezius on the ventrolateral region of the neck. Its origin is anterior to the levator scapula ventralis on the **mastoid** part of the skull and inserts with the clavotrapezius on the **clavicle.** The clavicle is very small in the cat and can be located most quickly by feel. The cleidomastoid is very closely associated with the sternomastoid along its median edge. The external jugular vein extends across the lateral surface of the sternomastoid but not across the cleidomastoid (see Fig. 34, *B*). In man these two muscles are usually merged with one another and are called "sternocleidomastoid," but occasionally they are similar to the cat. Do not bisect the cleidomastoid.

7. The **serratus anterior, or serratus ventralis,** arises on several ribs as separate myotomes and extends forward and dorsalward, passing between the scapula and the chest wall to insert on the inner upper edge of the scapula. In the upper portion, median to the scapula, the myotomes are merged into a compact muscle, with little indication of its myotome units. This muscle was first named in man, where the body is in an upright position and the muscle is really in an anterior position. The myotome origin on the ribs is serrated, which means notched. In the cat this muscle pulls the scapula posteriorward and downward. **Do not bisect this muscle.**

8. The **levator scapula** lies immediately in front of the serratus anterior and is continuous with it, so that the two muscles may appear as one. Pull the upper edge of the scapula away from the thoracic wall and see that these two muscles are continuous with one another. The transverse colli artery, a branch of the costocervical artery (Fig. 57), comes through the body wall and near the line of fusion. The levator scapula may be seen median to the lower part of the levator scapula ventralis, previously identified. The levator scapula pulls the scapula forward and toward the sternum. **Do not bisect this muscle, since it and the serratus anterior are left to hold the leg to the body.**

9. The **supraspinatus** covers the upper lateral surface of scapula, which is the supraspinatus fossa. It arises along the whole surface of the supraspinatus fossa. Its fibers converge to a point at the shoulder, pass over the shoulder joint, and insert on the **greater tuberosity of the humerus,** anterior to the acromiodeltoid. Do not dissect nor bisect.

10. The **infraspinatus** occupies the infraspinatus fossa on the outer side of the scapula below the spine. It arises from the fossa and spine of the scapula, the acromion, and the metacromion processes and converges into a tendon that is attached to the outside of the greater tuberosity of the humerus. Do not dissect nor bisect.

11. The **teres major** lies along the lower posterior edge of the scapula and passes forward and downward, median to the muscles of the upper arm. It merges with the latissimus dorsi. It can be loosened from the lower half of the edge of the scapula close to the point at which it merges with the latissimus dorsi and other muscles. Bisect and reflect the lower half only.

12. The **teres minor.** Reflect the lower half of the spinodeltoid and upper half of the acromiodeltoid; then the teres minor may be separated from what appears to be a part of the lower edge of the infraspinatus. It arises from the lower edge of the scapula, median to the upper portion of the acromiodeltoid, and inserts on the great tuberosity of the humerus below the infraspinatus. Do not bisect. Remember

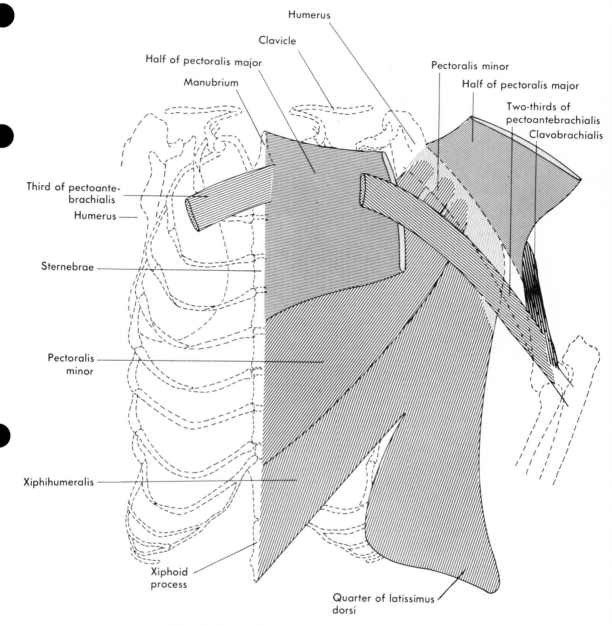

Fig. 26. Pectoralis muscles of chest, ventral view.

that these muscles should not be mutilated but should be left so they may be identified again later.

VENTRAL VIEW OF PECTORALIS MUSCLES OF CHEST, OR THORAX (Fig. 26)

Lay the cat on its back in a dissecting tray. Spread the legs apart and tie them securely.

Now you are ready to dissect and study the **pectoralis muscles** of the chest. They arise on the bones of the **sternum** and extend laterally to the **humerus** of each front leg. Examine the mounted skeleton of the cat to refresh your memory of the exact locations of the **manubrium, sternebrae,** and **xiphoid portions** of the sternum.

As you dissect the pectoralis muscles of the left chest, you will find that they do not separate or dissect off from one another as easily as most of the preceding muscles. There are four pectoralis muscles in the cat, but they are fused so closely with one another that they appear almost as one muscle. In Fig. 26 the part of the muscle shown on the right side indicates that it has been reflected. The smaller is the pecto-antibrachialis.

1. The **pectoantibrachialis** is about one-half inch wide, arises from the posterior part of the manubrium, passes laterally tight against the pectoralis major muscle, and merges with the **clavobrachialis** at about the middle of the humerus. It continues as a flat tendon and inserts on the ulna. Action pulls the arm medianward. Often, thin white lines indicate the edges. Loosen these edges and insert a probe under this thin, ribbonlike muscle, bisect, and reflect. The proximal end is shown reflected in Fig. 26.

2. The **pectoralis major** is two or three inches wide and lies immediately dorsal to the pectoantibrachialis. It is folded on itself and may appear as two or more parts. Its anterior edge is short, extending from the manubrium, ventral to the first rib and to the head of the humerus. It often merges with the sternomastoid and clavobrachialis. The origin is on the sternum from the manubrium to the fifth or seventh rib, and it inserts along most of the lateral surface of the humerus. The posterior edge may be determined by the difference in the direction of its fibers from those of the pectoralis minor, which lies posterior and dorsal to it (see Fig. 26). Loosen the pectoralis major along its anterior and posterior edges and insert a probe under its entire width—this is difficult because the muscle may be in several parts and folded upon itself. Bisect and reflect. Its distal end is shown reflected in Fig. 26.

3. The **pectoralis minor** lies partly dorsal and posterior to the pectoralis major, and its fibers extend obliquely. Its origin is on the sternum from the fourth to twelfth ribs; it inserts near the proximal end of the humerus, usually by thin fascia. Sometimes it divides into the anterior and posterior sections. The fibers of this muscle are loosely associated with one another, and along its posterior edge it is fused with the following muscle so completely that the line of separation is indefinite. Bisect the pectoralis minor in a straight line at right angles to its fibers. Reflect its proximal end to the sternum and expose the anterior thoracic vein. On the lateral surface is the long thoracic vein; you should also see the thoracic artery and second thoracic nerve entering the pectoralis muscles.

4. The **xiphihumeralis** is perhaps the most difficult of the pectoralis group to understand. Its fibers are parallel to and fuse with the posterior edge of the pectoralis minor. It is identified from the fact that its fibers arise on the xiphoid process of the sternum. It inserts on the humerus, but its fibers merge so completely with the **pectoralis minor** and **latissimus dorsi muscles** that its identity is lost.

These four muscles of the cat are represented in man by two, the pectoralis major and pectoralis minor. When these are cut on the cat, the axillary artery and vein and also the nerves of the brachial plexus may be seen passing from the body to the limb. Dissect away the fat and other connective tissue so they may be clearly seen. The arteries are red and the veins blue. Compare the cat muscles with those of man (Fig. 27).

When comparing the nerve supply of the pectoralis group of muscles in cat and man, the pectoantibrachialis and xiphihumeralis of the cat appear to have merged with the other two muscles in man. The general belief among anatomists is that when comparing similar structures in two closely related animals the structure having the least number of parts is considered the more specialized and higher but that the structures are homologous.

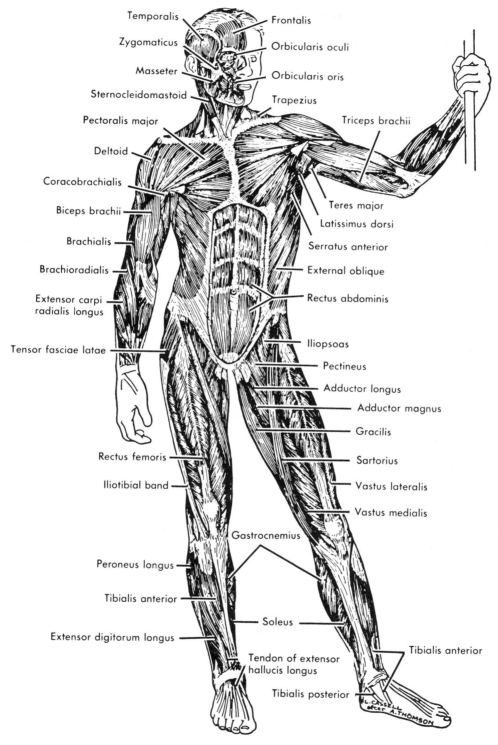

Fig. 27. Anterior view of the muscles of the human body. (From Millard, N. D., King, B. G., and Showers, M. J.: Human anatomy and physiology, Philadelphia, 1956, W. B. Saunders Co.)

43

REVIEW QUESTIONS ON MUSCLES OF NECK AND THORAX

1. How does one determine the origin and the insertion of a muscle?

2. Name five muscles that insert on the scapula. (Figs. 25 and 26)

3. Name five muscles that originate on the scapula. (Figs. 24 and 25)

4. Name three muscles that merge with the latissimus dorsi. (Examine your dissection; Fig. 29)

5. Which muscle attached to the scapula shows its myotomes, or muscle plates, most clearly? (Fig. 25)

6. Name three muscles that arise at the middorsal line near the thoracic neural spines. (Figs. 24 and 25)

7. Name three skeletal muscles that show progressive fusion of myotomes. (Figs. 24 and 25)

8. Where do the mammary glands lie in reference to the cutaneous maximus muscle? (See the dissected specimen of a lactating cat.)

9. State the origin and the insertion of the levator scapula and of the levator scapula ventralis muscles. (Fig. 25)

10. Name two locations where smooth, or nonstriated, muscles are found.

11. Name and locate two integumentary muscles. (Fig. 24)

12. What is the position of the brachiocephalic vein in reference to the shoulder muscles? (Fig. 24)

13. Name the muscles that attach the forelimb and the pectoral girdle to the body. (Figs. 24 and 25)

14. What is peculiar about the naming of the rhomboideus muscles in the cat? (Examine your specimen and read the directions; Fig. 25)

15. What is the advantage to the cat in having the pectoral girdle attached by muscles to the body and spinal column?

16. What is the advantage to the cat in having the pelvic girdle attached directly to the bones of the sacrum?

17. Define a "raphe" and give two examples. (See definitions of terms.)

18. Define a "symphysis" and give two examples. (See definition of terms.)

19. Name the four principal groups of skeletal muscles.

20. What is the general conclusion usually formed after considering comparable structures in closely related or in different species of vertebrate animals?

LATERAL MUSCLES OF LEFT BRACHIUM, OR UPPER ARM (Fig. 28)

1. The **triceps brachii** consists of several muscles on the posterior and lateral surfaces of the humerus. They are separated into three portions: (A) caput lateralis, (B) caput longus, and (C) caput mediale.

(A) The **caput lateralis**, or **lateral head,** is on the lateral surface of the upper arm immediately posterior to the clavobrachialis and brachialis anticus but is much larger and extends the entire length of the humerus. Its posterior edge can be easily separated from the muscle posterior to it.

Loosen the edges of the caput lateralis along the lateral surface of the upper arm from its origin on the upper surface of the humerus to the insertion on the ulna. Bisect and reflect as in Fig. 28. Observe the circumflex humeral artery along the median surface of the upper half of the reflected part of the caput lateralis.

(B) The **caput longus** is about twice as large as the previous muscle and lies along the posterior surface of the upper arm. It originates median to the spinodeltoid and teres major from the lower border of the scapula, and it inserts on the **olecranon pro-**

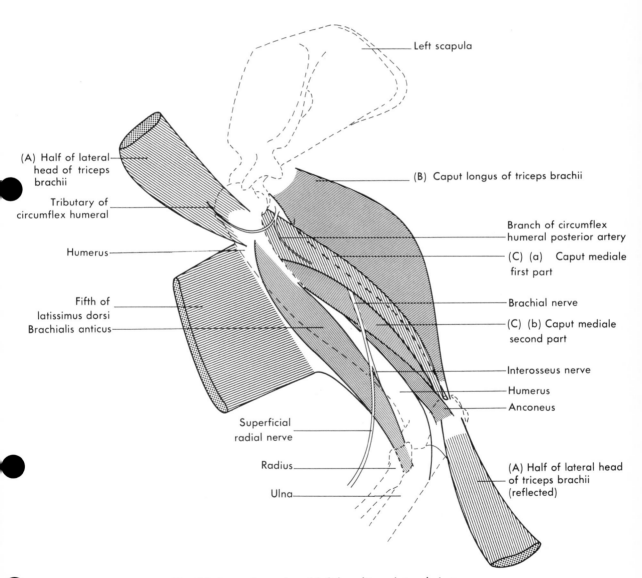

Fig. 28. Lateral muscles of left brachium, lateral view.

47

cess. Reflect the upper portion of the spinodeltoid to find the upper anterior edge. Before bisecting loosen the epitrochlean muscle, which is on the median surface of the upper arm. The **epitrochlean** (Fig. 29) is quite thin and flat on the posterior half of the median surface, and its upper end merges with the latissimus dorsi. Bisect the epitrochlean so that the median surface of the caput longus may be seen. Now bisect the caput longus.

(C) The **caput mediale**, or **median head**, consists of three parts:

(1) The **first part** ([C] [a]) (Fig. 28) arises from the posterior upper third of the humerus, anterior to the **caput longus**, passes downward, and joins the second part of the

caput mediale ([C][b]) about two-thirds the distance to the olecranon process. The **radial nerve** passes between the first and second parts of the median head of the triceps brachii and extends out on the lateral surface of the second part of the median head. It soon divides into the long **superficial radial nerve** to the forearm and the **interosseus nerve** to the muscles of the elbow. Do not bisect this part of the muscle.

(2) The **second part** ([C][b]) of the median head of the triceps muscle, which arises from about the middle third of the posterior surface of the **humerus**, lies parallel to the first part, and together they pass to the upper surface of the olecranon process.

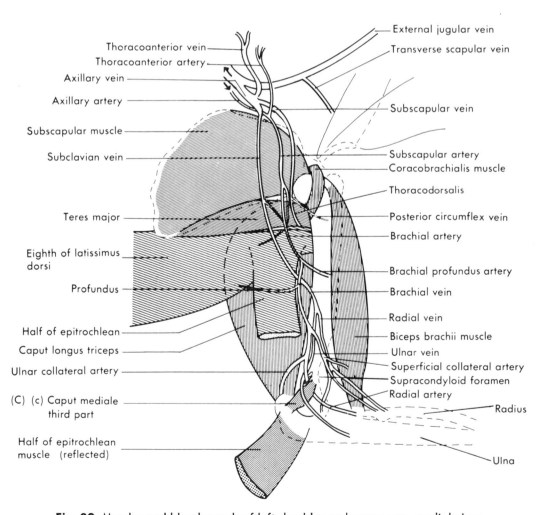

Fig. 29. Muscles and blood vessels of left shoulder and upper arm, medial view.

(3) The **third part** ([C][c]), or **caput mediale** (Fig. 29) portion, of the triceps brachii muscle is about one inch in length and lies on the inner or median surface of the lower end of the humerus. It cannot be seen from the lateral surface. This part should not be confused with the anconeus muscle, which is on the lateral surface of the humerus. Therefore, **turn your cat so that its head will be to your right and its back toward you. Then turn the left front leg up over the cat's back** to get the median view of the leg, as in Fig. 29. If you have a left humerus bone, examine its supracondyloid foramen as you read the following description and place the bone on the cat in its proper position. In order to find the **supracondyloid foramen** reflect the lower portion of the epitrochlean muscle, previously bisected, and dissect off the connective tissue from the supracondy-

loid foramen and the inner surface of the olecranon process. Identify the **radial artery**, which accompanies the median nerve as they pass through the supracondyloid foramen. Insert a small probe into this foramen. Now we should be able to identify this small muscle. This **third part of the caput mediale muscle** arises from the part of the humerus that forms the arch of the supracondyloid foramen, passes posteriorly, and inserts on the inner surface of **the olecranon process**. This muscle is not shown in Fig. 28 but is included in Fig 29. Each of these parts of the triceps helps to extend the leg or forearm. When the three heads of the triceps brachii muscle contract, they straighten out the front leg quickly, enabling the cat to force the thorax and head up. At about the same time the muscles of the hind legs give the propelling power for the long jump.

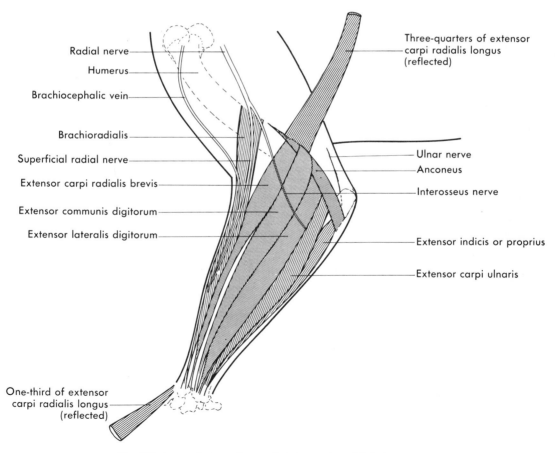

Radial nerve
Humerus
Brachiocephalic vein

Brachioradialis
Superficial radial nerve
Extensor carpi radialis brevis
Extensor communis digitorum
Extensor lateralis digitorum

Three-quarters of extensor carpi radialis longus (reflected)

Ulnar nerve
Anconeus
Interosseus nerve

Extensor indicis or proprius

Extensor carpi ulnaris

One-third of extensor carpi radialis longus (reflected)

Fig. 30. Lateral view of superficial muscles of left forearm.

We come now to the second main division of the muscles of the brachium, or upper arm.

2. The **brachialis anticus** arises on the lateral surface of the upper part of the humerus and inserts on the median surface of the **ulna.** Reflect the lower half of the acromiodeltoid and dissect off the fascia below its insertion. The brachialis anticus lies lateral to the insertion of the pectoralis major close against the lateral surface of the humerus. It inserts on the median surface of the ulna below the semilunar notch and helps to bend the foreleg. It is the same in man. Do not bisect.

3. The **anconeus** is easily confused with the third part of the median head of the triceps brachii muscle ([C] [c], Fig. 29), which is on the inner or median side of the arm. The anconeus, however, is on the outer or lateral side of the lower part of the humerus (Figs. 28 and 30) and inserts on the lower edge of the semilunar notch of the ulna and thus supports the elbow joint. Turn your specimen so that you get the lateral view of the left front leg and identify the anconeus distal to the second part of the median head of the triceps. Color the muscles red and leave the bones and nerves white in Fig. 28.

MEDIAN MUSCLES OF LEFT SHOULDER AND UPPER ARM (Fig. 29)

Again turn your cat around so that its head is to your right and its back toward you. Now turn its left leg up over the back toward you so you can more easily examine the median, or inner, surface of the scapula and brachium of the left foreleg.

1. The **subscapularis** fills the entire subscapular fossa on the median side of the scapula. Its origin is the entire subscapular fossa, except in the area of attachment of the levator scapula and the serratus anterior. Its insertion is by a flat tendon into the dorsal border of the lesser tuberosity of the humerus. The **teres major** muscle, previously identified, lies ventral to the lower edge of the scapula. Ventral to the teres major is a part of the anterior end of the **latissimus dorsi.** These two muscles come forward median to the long head of the

triceps and insert on the **humerus.** They are the same in man. The subscapularis acts as an adductor of the humerus.

2. The **coracobrachialis,** about one-half inch long, is on the inner side of the shoulder joint and covers the insertion of the subscapularis muscle. It arises by a rounded tendon from the apex of the coracoid process. Fleshy fibers insert on the medial surface of the humerus near its proximal end and above the insertion of the teres major. It is the same in man. It acts as an adductor of the humerus. Do not bisect.

3. The **biceps brachii** is large and spindle shaped, lying on the anterior surface of the **humerus,** median to the insertion of the pectoralis major. Do not confuse it with the brachialis anticus. The biceps brachii arises by a strong tendon from the anterior margin of the glenoid cavity of the scapula. The tendon passes laterally along the bicipital tuberosity of the humerus. It is the same in man, except that the muscle arises by two heads. It acts as the flexor of the forearm and the supinator, since it turns the arm so the palm is upward. Bisect.

4. The **epitrochlean,** or extensor antibrachialis longus, should have been bisected in locating the parts of the triceps, and the lower part is reflected in Fig. 29. It is an exceptionally thin muscle on the median side of the upper arm. It arises on the fascia of the lateral surface of the ventral border of the latissimus dorsi and inserts by a broad tendon onto the olecranon process. Sometimes it merges with the fascia of the pectoantibrachialis. The epitrochlean is not found in man. It extends the foreleg and helps turn the palm upward.

5. **Arteries.** Observe the **axillary artery** as it comes through the thoracic wall to supply the shoulder and foreleg. Do not cut the serratus anterior nor the levator scapula muscles, since they should be left to hold the leg to the body. The axillary artery gives off the **thoracoanterior** to the pectoralis muscles immediately lateral to the body wall. The **subscapular artery** gives off a branch passing between the **subscapular** and the **teres major muscles.** The main artery, now known as the **brachial,** passes medially to the humerus, where it gives

off the **brachial profundus** to the **biceps muscle** and further on the **superficial collateral artery,** which passes close to the distal end of the biceps brachii muscle and onto the radial side of the forearm. As the brachial artery approaches the elbow joint, it divides into the **radial artery,** which passes through the **supracondyloid foramen** of the humerus, and the **ulnar artery,** which passes median to the olecranon process. The latter three arteries pass into the forearm and subdivide to supply various muscles controlling the digits.

6. **Veins.** The **axillary vein** enters the thoracic wall below or posterior to the **external jugular** and continues as the **subclavian** under the clavicle. The main tributary to the axillary portion of the subclavian is the brachial.

The **brachial vein** lies on the median side of the upper arm or brachium and receives a small vein, the **profundus brachii,** from the biceps muscle, usually coming between the teres major and the latissimus dorsi. This vein is incompletely shown in Fig. 29. In the lower portion of the upper arm the brachial vein is formed by the union of the **radial** and **ulnar veins.** The **axillary vein** receives the **thoracoanterior** and also the **subscapular,** usually immediately lateral to the thoracic wall, but the entrance position of the latter varies considerably in different cats. Trace the subscapular vein to where it comes from between the teres major and the latissimus dorsi.

The large **external jugular vein** comes down the ventrolateral surface of the neck and enters the thorax anterior to the axillary vein. The external jugular lies almost immediately under the skin and receives the **transverse scapular vein** a few centimeters before it enters the thorax. The transverse scapular vein usually receives the **brachiocephalic** from the lateral surface of the shoulder and upper arm (Figs. 30 and 52), which was identified when beginning the dissection of the muscles. The **posterior circumflex vein** branches from the brachiocephalic in the region of the acromiodeltoid muscle and passes in deeply to connect with the subscapular vein. The

posterior circumflex can be seen in Fig. 29 posterior and on a level with the head of the humerus between the insertions of the teres major and latissimus dorsi muscles, where it becomes continuous with the subscapular or joins the brachial, which is a tributary of the subclavian vein. In man all blood from the brachiocephalic vein passes by way of the **posterior circumflex** to the subscapular, and none enters the transverse scapular. Unless the veins are well injected, you will probably be unable to identify them. Occasionally a marked variation from the normal in position or structure is found; this is an anomaly. The size of the vein when injected depends largely on the amount of material and pressure used when injecting. These vessels will be considered again when the venous system as a whole is studied.

7. **Nerves.** Some of the principal nerves may be identified at this time. They are as follows: (a) The **median** is the easiest to identify, since it has three long roots that unite almost at the same level as the head of the humerus; trace it until it passes through the supracondyloid foramen of the humerus with the radial artery. (b) The **ulnar** is the most posterior of the three largest nerves and becomes superficial, where it is easily exposed as the "crazy bone" or "funny bone" against the median condyle of the humerus; it then continues over the olecranon process. (c) The **radial** extends diagonally across the humerus, as shown in Figs. 28 and 30, and divides into the **superficial radial** and the **interosseous nerves.** Color the blood vessels and add arrows to show the direction of flow.

LATERAL VIEW OF SUPERFICIAL LATERAL MUSCLES OF LEFT FOREARM (Fig. 30)

Examine the lateral surface of the left forearm. The olecranon process is sometimes incorrectly called the "crazy bone" or "funny bone." The lower part of the humerus, at the place where the **ulnar nerve** is "close" to the inner surface of the elbow, is the "crazy bone." Dissect off several layers of connective tissue, or fascia, from the lateral surface of the forearm, being careful not to injure the underlying muscles. These muscles are so much alike that it is difficult to remember them accurately unless they are studied in some definite order. Therefore, we will take them in order, beginning with the one most anterior and proceeding to the one most posterior, as seen from the lateral surface. Identify each muscle at or near its origin on the humerus near the edge of the **anconeus** and trace it distally.

1. The **brachioradialis** muscle is on the lateral surface of the humerus below the lower end of the acromiodeltoid, median to the **superficial radial nerve** but lateral to the brachialis anticus. It gradually decreases in size as it extends down the anterolateral surface of the radius and parallel with the superficial radial nerve, and it inserts on the styloid process of the radius. The **brachiocephalic vein** passes up the anterior portion of the leg and the brachioradialis muscle. Color the veins blue and the nerves green in the drawing. Bisect but do not damage the vein.

2. The **extensor carpi radialis longus** has a broad origin and is larger and distal to the **brachioradialis,** but it has about the same general proportions. It extends down the lateral surface of the radius. Its distal third is a small tendon inserted on the dorsal surface of the second metacarpal. It lies against and is often fused with the following muscle. Its function is to help extend the paw. Bisect distally to the former muscle. This muscle is shown reflected in Fig. 30.

3. The **extensor carpi radialis brevis** is usually partly covered by the previous muscle, particularly the upper end. It is often fused with the previous muscle, but it ends in a slender, short tendon on the third metacarpal. The **deep interosseus branch** of the radial nerve passes under the head of this muscle. This muscle helps to extend the paw. Do not bisect. The following three muscles originate on the humerus beneath the **anconeus muscle,** previously considered in the group of lateral brachial muscles.

4. The **extensor communis digitorum** is exposed laterally for the entire length down the lateral surface of the arm; the middle third merges gradually into a slender muscular tendon. The tendon divides at the wrist and attaches to the second, third, fourth, and fifth digits, which it extends. Dissect out and bisect at a different level than that for former muscles.

5. The **extensor lateralis digitorum** (corresponds to the extensor digiti quinti proprius of man) has about the same appearance as the former muscle, but it is usually slightly broader, lies lateral to the ulna, and divides to each of the third, fourth, and fifth digits. It extends these digits. Bisect distal to that of number four.

6. The **extensor carpi ulnaris** originates from the lateral epicondyle of the humerus and extends down the arm lateral to the region separating the radius and ulna. It is rather uniform in size and often has a shiny tendon. It inserts on the tubercle on the ulnar side of the base of the fifth metacarpal. Bisect distal to that of number five.

7. The **extensor indicis (proprius)** is small and arises immediately caudad to the origin of the extensor carpi ulnaris on the anterolateral surface of the ulna by short, fleshy fibers below and lateral to the semilunar notch. Fibers extend distally and toward the radius, tight against the ulna. The lower half has a white, shiny tendon. Much of this muscle lies median to the extensor carpi ulnaris and supplies the second digit, or it may go to the first three.

These muscles have long tendons attached to the bones of the toes. Tendons differ from ligaments in that they extend from muscles to bones, while ligaments extend from bone to bone.

If the muscles are becoming dry, place damp paper towels or cloth under the skin before wrapping and putting away at the end of each laboratory period.

DEEP LATERAL MUSCLES OF LEFT FOREARM, OR ANTIBRACHIUM (Fig. 31)

Now reflect the proximal ends of the preceding muscles (two to five) and find the interosseous nerve, which extends laterally to the origin of the following muscles.

1. The **supinator** is flat, slightly spiral, and extends down the lateral and anterior

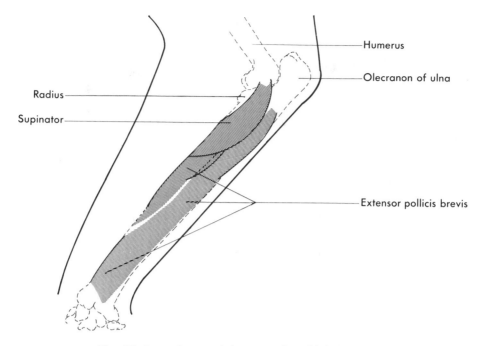

Fig. 31. Lateral view of deep muscles of left forearm.

surfaces on the proximal end of the radius. It arises by ligaments from the lateral surface of the humerus and the upper outer surface of the radius. It passes distally and medially, converges, covers the upper surface of the radius, and inserts on the proximal third of the ventral surface of the radius. Do not bisect.

2. The **extensor brevis pollicis** extends from the distal anterior surface of the ulna and from the posterior surface of the lateral third of the radius. Fibers converge to form a flat tendon that passes obliquely over tendons of the extensor carpi radialis longus and brevis on the anterolateral surface of the wrist. Do not bisect.

MEDIAN VIEW OF SUPERFICIAL MEDIAN MUSCLES OF LEFT FOREARM (Fig. 32)

Turn the cat so that its head is to your right and its back is toward you. Turn the left foreleg up over the back in the position shown in Fig. 32; dissect off several layers of heavy fascia from the median, or inner, side of the left foreleg. In Fig. 32 the lower parts of the **epitrochlean** and the **third part of the caput mediale of the triceps** are shown near the elbow. The **brachioradialis** and the **extensor carpi radialis brevis** are shown on the inner side of the bend, with their origins on the lateral surface of the humerus. These muscles were identified in the previous exercise but should be recognized from this view so that they may not be confused with others.

1. The **pronator teres** arises from the median epicondyle of the humerus near the lower end of the bony arch forming the supracondyloid foramen. It passes distally parallel with and caudad to the radial artery. It decreases definitely in size, and its lower half may be difficult to trace to its insertion on the radius. Do not bisect.

2. The **extensor carpi radialis brevis** is partially seen between the supinator and the extensor brevis pollicis. It extends the phalanges.

3. The **flexor carpi radialis** originates on the median epicondyle of the humerus, distal to the origin of the previous muscle; it extends distally to a more anterior position at the lower end of the radius, gradually tapering into a small tendon lateral to the radial artery. The outer anterior surface is against the pronator teres, and the posterior

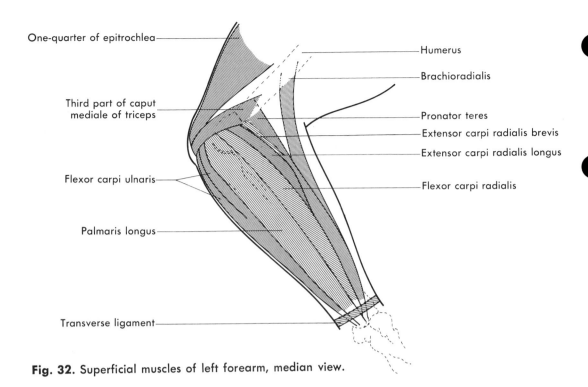

One-quarter of epitrochlea

Humerus

Brachioradialis

Third part of caput mediale of triceps

Pronator teres

Extensor carpi radialis brevis

Extensor carpi radialis longus

Flexor carpi ulnaris

Flexor carpi radialis

Palmaris longus

Transverse ligament

Fig. 32. Superficial muscles of left forearm, median view.

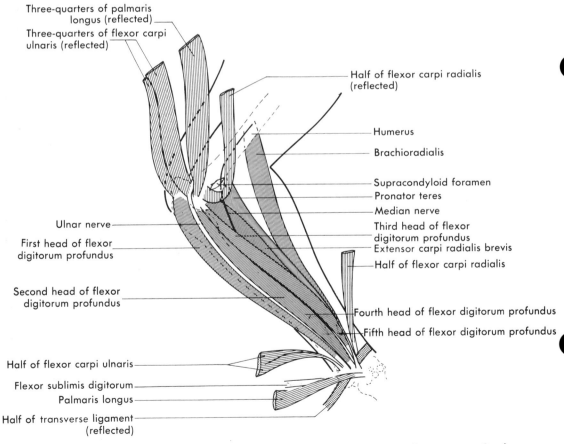

Three-quarters of palmaris longus (reflected)

Three-quarters of flexor carpi ulnaris (reflected)

Half of flexor carpi radialis (reflected)

Humerus

Brachioradialis

Supracondyloid foramen

Pronator teres

Median nerve

Ulnar nerve

Third head of flexor digitorum profundus

First head of flexor digitorum profundus

Extensor carpi radialis brevis

Half of flexor carpi radialis

Second head of flexor digitorum profundus

Fourth head of flexor digitorum profundus

Fifth head of flexor digitorum profundus

Half of flexor carpi ulnaris

Flexor sublimis digitorum

Palmaris longus

Half of transverse ligament (reflected)

Fig. 33. Median view of deep muscles of left forearm of the flexor digitorum profundus group.

surface is against the third head of the flexor digitorum profundus and sometimes the palmaris longus. The radial artery often lies on the lower half of this muscle. Bisect and reflect as shown in Fig. 33.

4. The **palmaris longus** is a large, flat, broad muscle in the center of the median surface. It arises from the epicondyle of the humerus, with its small head supplied by the ulnar artery. It ends in a flat tendon at the wrist, passes through the **transverse ligament,** divides into several tendons, and spreads out into a pad in the palm of the hand, which divides, giving off tendons to the digits. Bisect and reflect.

5. The **flexor digitorum sublimus** has an **ulnar** and a **radial part.** Cut and reflect the **transverse ligament** at the wrist and dissect out the lower end of the palmaris longus muscle as shown in Fig. 33. The ulnar part of the flexor digitorum sublimus originates from the lower lateral surface of the palmaris longus. The radial part arises from the area of merging of the tendons from the first and second parts of the flexor digitorum profundus but soon divides and supplies the second and third digits. Do not bisect. This muscle is much larger in man.

6. The **flexor carpi ulnaris** appears to have two heads. One arises on the median epicondyle of the humerus, the other on the median part of the olecranon process of the ulna. The two heads may be separated by the **ulnar nerve** and pass down as separate muscles almost to the wrist, where they unite into one tendon to be inserted onto the bones of the wrist. They act to bend or flex the wrist. Bisect and reflect, cutting through the lower third.

MEDIAN VIEW OF DEEPER MUSCLES OF LEFT FOREARM (FLEXOR DIGITORUM PROFUNDUS GROUP) (Fig. 33)

Keep the specimen in the same position as when dissecting the former group of muscles.

As in Fig. 33 muscles one, three, and four of the previous group are shown reflected to expose the flexor digitorum profundus group of muscles. This group is called one muscle but really appears as five parts or heads. These five muscles are more or less fused with one another, but this is different in each cat. Hence, the following description may not be entirely accurate. They are considered from the ulna forward toward the radius. They function in bending the ends of the toes.

1. The **first head,** or **part,** is under the posterior head of the **flexor carpi ulnaris** on the median posterior surface of the ulna. It extends distally, is the largest of the five, is uniform in size, and is closely attached to the median surface of the ulna. Do not loosen nor bisect.

2. The **second head** arises from the distal end of the median epicondyle of the humerus anterior to the **ulnar nerve,** which separates the first and second heads of the flexor digitorum profundus down to the wrist. Loosen the nerve and see where it passes over the elbow, where it is called the "crazy bone" in man. The **flexor carpi ulnaris** covers most of the first two heads. The second, third, and fourth heads are more or less fused with one another, and the way they fuse with one another varies in different cats. Do not force their separation. Bisect the second head and find the fourth head, which is usually directly under it.

The third, fourth, and fifth heads vary greatly in their size and fusion with one another.

3. The **third head** arises from the median epicondyle of the humerus, under the heads of the **palmaris longus** and **flexor carpi radialis.** It lies anterior to and, throughout most of its length, in contact with the second head. Its proximal portion merges with the fourth head, but distal parts are separate before reaching the wrist. Do not bisect.

4. The **fourth head** arises from the median epicondyle of the humerus under the second head, with which it is closely associated or fused halfway to the wrist. The distal portion usually decreases in size abruptly into a small definite tendon. In some cases the fourth head is fused with the first, but their distal ends can usually be separated, as shown in Fig. 33. Do not

force the separation of these heads or parts.

5. The **fifth head** arises from the upper third of the radius, and its fibers are in contact with the **pronator teres** under the third head. The fifth head joins the third at the wrist, where it is probably easiest identified and where it is shown in Fig. 33. If you have a small cat, the fifth head may be difficult to identify. It lies close against the median surface of the ulna and forms a flat, muscular tendon between the lower ends of the ulna and radius. The radial artery and vein and branches of the median nerve are conspicuous along the median side of the radius.

In man the flexor digitorum profundus group is a single large muscle covering the ulnar side of the forearm. It arises mostly from the upper ventral and median surfaces of the ulna and ends in four tendons supplying the second to the fifth digits.

The **pronator quadratus** is not a part of the flexor digitorum profundus group. It is seen under the fifth head, however. Its fibers extend from the lower end of the ulna distally and forward to join the radius distal to those of the fifth head. Its fibers are deeper and extend at an oblique angle to those of the fifth head.

REVIEW QUESTIONS ON MUSCLES OF BRACHIUM AND FOREARM

1. What is the advantage to the cat in having the triceps muscles larger and stronger than the biceps and brachialis anticus?

2. Name two large muscles attached on the olecranon process of the ulna. (Figs. 28 and 29)

3. Name the muscles inserted on the humerus close to the biceps and the brachialis anticus muscles. (Fig. 28)

4. Name two small muscles that originate on the distal end of the humerus and insert on the ulna. (Figs. 29 and 30)

5. Name the two largest muscles inserted on the humerus. (Figs. 26 and 29)

6. What structures pass through the supracondyloid foramen? (Figs. 29 and 72)

7. How many muscles or parts constitute the profundus group of muscles? (Fig. 33)

8. What is the difference between a tendon and a ligament? (See definition of terms.)

9. What advantage is there in having long, narrow tendons extending over the carpal and metacarpal bones to the various digits? (Fig. 33)

10. Name two small muscles with origins on the scapula and insertions on the humerus. (Fig. 24)

11. Name three large muscles between the scapula and the ribs. (Fig. 25)

12. Name a small muscle of the shoulder that inserts on the humerus. (Fig. 29)

13. Name two small muscles of the elbow that originate on the humerus. (Figs. 28 and 29)

14. What constitutes the so-called "crazy bone"? (Fig. 33)

15. What is the olecranon process, and what is its function in relation to movements of the forearm? (Examine your specimen; Fig. 11)

16. Where are the principal blood vessels located in reference to the upper arm and humerus? (See your specimen; Fig. 29)

17. What is the general function of the profundus group of muscles? (Fig. 33)

18. Where are the muscles that control the principal movements of the toes located? (Examine your specimen; Fig. 33)

VENTRAL MUSCLES OF
NECK AND LOWER JAW
(Fig. 34, A to C)

Pass a probe under the pectoralis group of muscles; bisect, if not previously done, and reflect to expose the smaller muscles close to the ribs, as shown in Fig. 34, A.

1. The **sternalis,** or **transverse costarum,** and its ligaments (Fig. 34, A) extend over the first five ribs. It extends from the sternum at about the base of the fifth rib diagonally toward the clavicle but inserts on the first and second ribs. It assists in bracing the chest wall. Loosen its edges and bisect. This muscle is absent in man.

2. The **scalenus** is long and slender; it extends lateral to the sternalis but also ventral to most of the thorax from the ninth rib forward dorsal to the **external jugular vein** and the **mastoid muscle** to attach to the transverse processes of the cervical vertebrae. Loosen the edges of this vein and also those of the sternomastoid muscle, finding the myotomes going to some of the ribs. Do not bisect. Observe the tributaries of the **external jugular vein** as follows: (a) The **transverse jugular** extends across near the **hyoid cartilage** or bone to join the external jugular on the opposite side (Fig 34). (b) The **anterior facial vein** arises over the lateral edge of the mouth. (c) The **posterior facial vein** enters the external jugular near the base of the ear, ventral to the **submaxillary salivary gland.** The **anterior** and **posterior auricular** tributaries usually unite with one another below the **parotid salivary gland,** which is below the ear. Two usually large **lymph glands** lie close to the anterior facial vein (Fig. 34, B), and one lies posterior to the submaxillary gland. All lymph glands eventually drain by capillary tubules into the lymphatic system. The **sublingual salivary gland** is small and deeply located immediately anterior to and in touch with the submaxillary gland. The **internal maxillary artery** passes close to it.

(3) The **external oblique muscle** covers most of the lateral abdominal wall. Its fibers pass posteriorly and ventrally. Its sheaths or broad ligaments only originate at the middorsal line and terminate at the midventral line. At about the eighth rib find the anterior edge of the muscle fibers, loosen the edge, carefully pass a small probe under the muscle fibers, and bisect along line xy (Fig. 34, A). Reflect the ventral portion of this muscle as shown on the left side of the cat. Observe that the heavy **fascia,** or **aponeurosis,** acts as a sheath over the **rectus abdominis** muscle to the midventral line.

(4) The **rectus abdominis** extends from the sternalis to the pubic symphysis immediately lateral to the midventral line. Reflect the bisected portion of the external oblique to uncover a part of the rectus abdominis (see Fig. 35).

(5) The **sternomastoid** arises on the manubrium and extends anterolaterally dorsal to the jugular veins and inserts on the mastoid part of the skull (Fig. 34, A). Each sternomastoid is almost triangular in shape with its base on the manubrium. However, each joins the other along the midventral line and then separates and narrows uniformly to the insertion (Fig. 34, A and B). Cut the bases of the two sternomastoid muscles apart along the median line (see Fig. 34, B). Pass a probe under the right one, bisect close to the clavicle, and reflect as shown on the right side in Fig. 34, A.

(6) The **cleidomastoid** arises on the **clavicle,** passes dorsally and laterally to the **sternomastoid,** and inserts on the skull close to the sternomastoid. It was identified previously in the lateral view of the deep muscles of the neck and shoulder (Fig. 25). In man the lower ends of the cleidomastoid and sternomastoid muscles are separate, but they are fused throughout most of their course and together are known as the sternocleidomastoid muscle. Turn your head to the left as far as you can and feel it on the right side of your neck. These muscles, separately or together, help to pull the head ventrolaterally.

(7) The **sternohyoid** arises on the manubrium under the sternomastoid, passes forward close to the median line over the **cricoid** and **thyroid cartilages,** and inserts on the **hyoid cartilage.** Separate the two thin sternohyoid muscles along the median line, loosen the right one, bisect, reflect its

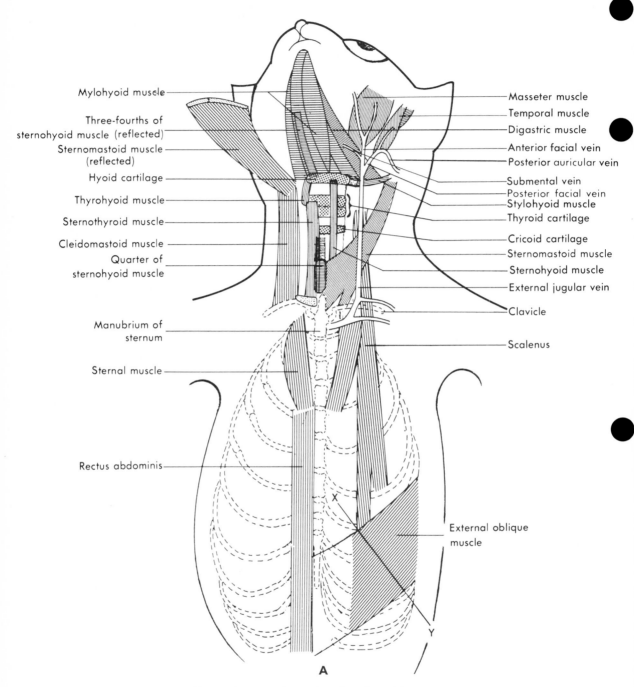

Fig. 34A. Ventral muscles of neck and lower jaw.

Mylohyoid muscle

Three-fourths of sternohyoid muscle (reflected)

Sternomastoid muscle (reflected)

Hyoid cartilage

Thyrohyoid muscle

Sternothyroid muscle

Cleidomastoid muscle

Quarter of sternohyoid muscle

Manubrium of sternum

Sternal muscle

Rectus abdominis

Masseter muscle

Temporal muscle

Digastric muscle

Anterior facial vein

Posterior auricular vein

Submental vein

Posterior facial vein

Stylohyoid muscle

Thyroid cartilage

Cricoid cartilage

Sternomastoid muscle

Sternohyoid muscle

External jugular vein

Clavicle

Scalenus

External oblique muscle

A

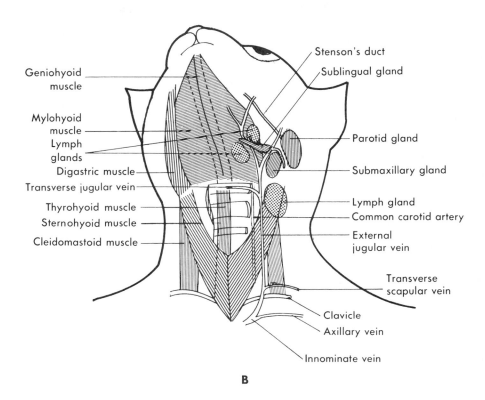

Geniohyoid muscle

Mylohyoid muscle

Lymph glands

Digastric muscle

Transverse jugular vein

Thyrohyoid muscle

Sternohyoid muscle

Cleidomastoid muscle

Stenson's duct

Sublingual gland

Parotid gland

Submaxillary gland

Lymph gland

Common carotid artery

External jugular vein

Transverse scapular vein

Clavicle

Axillary vein

Innominate vein

B

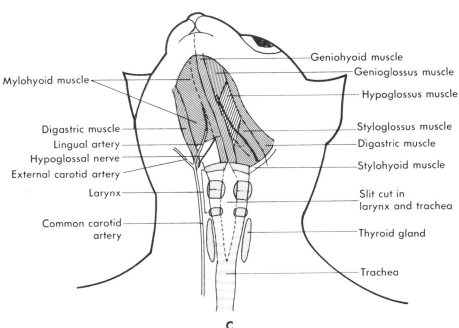

Mylohyoid muscle

Digastric muscle

Lingual artery

Hypoglossal nerve

External carotid artery

Larynx

Common carotid artery

Geniohyoid muscle

Genioglossus muscle

Hypoglossus muscle

Styloglossus muscle

Digastric muscle

Stylohyoid muscle

Slit cut in larynx and trachea

Thyroid gland

Trachea

C

Fig. 34,B. Superficial muscles of neck and lower jaw. **C,** Deeper muscles of neck and lower jaw.

61

anterior half as shown in Fig. 34, *A*, and find the sternothyroid immediately under it, as seen from ventral view.

BRANCHIAL MUSCLES

The following muscles, which extend from the lower jaw, or the **manubrium,** to cartilages of the larynx, are known collectively as the **branchial muscles,** since their homologues in fishes move the gills.

(1) The **sternothyroid** is shorter than the previous muscle, since it extends from the manubrium only to the thyroid cartilage. These last two named muscles help pull the larynx down when swallowing and are practically the same in man.

(2) The **thyrohyoid** extends from the lateral surface of the thyroid to the hyoid cartilage and is almost in line with the previous muscle. It is only about one-half inch long. Carefully dissect away the fascia, pass a probe under it, but do not bisect. Under the sternothyroid muscle is the trachea with its transverse cartilaginous rings. Rub these with your finger to help identify them. Lateral to the trachea and larynx is the common carotid artery (Fig. 34, *B*), which is usually injected with red latex. Lateral to the carotid artery is the vagosympathetic nerve trunk. Separate the larger vagus nerve from the sympathetic nerve on the right side of the cat. These nerves are shown in Fig. 71. The **thyroid gland** lies between the carotid artery and the upper end of the trachea and cricoid cartilage. It is cigar shaped, is reddish in color, similar to muscular tissue, and is held in place by loose connective tissue. Loosen the thyroid on the right side but do not remove it. It is one of the endocrine glands, and its **hormone** is drained away by blood. In man an abnormality of this gland is known as goiter.

(3) The **stylohyoid** muscle is about two millimeters wide and two centimeters long. It extends laterally from the base of the hyoid cartilage, dorsal to the external jugular vein and digastric muscle, between it and the lower jawbone, to the auditory bulla. Here it is attached to the long cornua or greater wing of the hyoid cartilage (see Fig. 34, *A*). The greater wing of the hyoid in the cat is homologous with the lesser

wing in man. The **stylohyoid** muscle is easily damaged or overlooked. It helps to pull the larynx up when swallowing. It is similar in man except that it is attached on the styloid process of the temporal bone.

(4) The **digastric** muscle lies close against the median surface of the lower jaw. It arises on the jugular and mastoid processes of the skull and inserts on the anterior half of the mandible and forward to the symphysis. The **anterior facial vein,** a tributary of the external jugular, crosses the digastric at the angle of the jaw and there receives the submental vein. This vein passes between the **digastric** and the jawbone. Pass a probe under the digastric at the angle of the jaw and bisect and reflect the anterior end to expose the mylohyoid muscle, whose fibers pass transversely from one jaw to the other. Reflect the caudal end of the digastric far enough to expose the **external carotid artery** on the right side (Fig. 34, *C*). Near the bend of this artery it branches into the **lingual** to the base of the tongue. The **hypoglossal nerve** passes forward almost parallel to this artery and dorsal to the posterior edge of the mylohyoid muscle. The **axillary vein** joins the **external jugular** (Fig. 34, *B*) near the thoracic wall and unites with the **subclavian vein.** At the base of the neck the **transverse scapular** joins the **external jugular.**

(5) The **mylohyoid** is thin and its fibers extend from the inner surface of each jaw to the median line where they meet the corresponding muscle from the opposite side along the raphe. Lift up its posterior edge on the right side (Fig. 34, *C*), starting where the hypoglossal nerve passes dorsal to it. Bisect and reflect the mylohyoid and find the narrow **geniohyoid** muscle extending near the median line from the hyoid cartilage to the symphysis of the mandible. Also reflect the sheath of fascia dorsal to the mylohyoid muscle, which contains branches of the hypoglossal nerve.

(6) Three small muscles, whose fibers contribute to the formation of the tongue, can now be identified as follows: (a) The **genioglossus** arises near the symphysis, extends parallel to the geniohyoid for a short distance, then passes dorsal to some small

muscles, and inserts on the base of the hyoid cartilage. (b) The **hypoglossus** extends obliquely immediately posterior to the origin of the genioglossus and the center of the mandible and inserts on the base of the hyoid cartilage. (c) The **styloglossus** lies dorsal and median to the **digastric**, whose fibers are almost parallel with the lower jaw. These three muscles are extrinsic to the tongue, but they also pass into it and assist in its movements and in the elevation of the larynx. They are much the same in man.

(7) The **masseter** is thick at the posterior outer surface of the lower jaw (Fig. 34, *A*). It arises from the zygomatic arch and inserts on the mandible at the ventral border of the coronoid fossa. It is the same in man. It elevates the lower jaw. Do not bisect.

(8) The **temporalis** is fan shaped and covers the temporal region of the skull in front of the ear and close to the temporal bone. It arises from the squamous portion of the temporal bone and inserts on the lateral and median surfaces of the coronoid border of the mandible. It helps elevate the lower jaw. Do not bisect. The hyoid, thyroid and cricoid cartilages, as well as the embryonic cartilaginous jaws, and also the malleus, incus, and stapes arise from embryonic branchial arches.

VEINS, LYMPH GLANDS, AND SALIVARY GLANDS (Fig. 34, A and B)

1. The external jugular vein is formed by three main tributaries at the base of the skull.

(a) The **transverse jugular** connects with the opposite side in the region of the hyoid cartilage.

(b) The **posterior facial** is from the region at the base of the ear.

(c) The **anterior facial** is from the upper and lower jaws. Dissect off the platysma muscle fibers and connective tissue to expose these veins.

2. The **lymph glands** in this region vary in size and position (Fig. 34, *B* and *C*).

Usually there is one or two near the base of the anterior facial vein; there is also often one large lymph gland lateral to the cartilages of the larynx. This one is the most variable.

3. Salivary glands include the parotid, submaxillary, and sublingual.

(a) The **parotid gland** lies ventral to the external auditory meatus. It is large and irregular in shape. It is drained by Stensen's duct, which passes forward laterally across the masseter muscle. It then turns medially and enters the mouth lateral to the upper third premolar tooth. Remove the connective tissue surrounding and covering the parotid gland.

(b) The **submaxillary gland** lies ventral to the parotid and usually in contact with it. It is smooth and more uniform in shape than the parotid. The posterior facial vein crosses its ventral surface and Wharton's duct drains it. Wharton's duct is small and passes laterally to the digastric muscle, then dorsal to the mylohyoid, and opens into the mouth by a large papilla near the frenulum, or median membrane, under the tongue.

(c) The **sublingual gland** (Fig. 34, *B*) is small, elongated, of slightly different color, and deeply situated at the anteromedian edge of the submaxillary gland. Do not confuse it with the larger more superficial lymph glands. The sublingual has two ducts, the **Rivinus** and the **Bartholin**, which extend nearly parallel with and open into the mouth near the opening of Wharton's duct. These ducts are difficult to identify. Cut the anterior facial vein near its base and reflect it and the submaxillary gland, to which the sublingual is attached. Now you should see the elongated sublingual; notice how it lies between the masseter and digastric muscles.

Slit open the larynx (Fig. 34, *C*) so that you can definitely feel and see the three cartilages. Pass a probe into the slit of the larynx dorsally and forward through the glottis into the pharynx and mouth (see Figs. 62 and 63).

REVIEW QUESTIONS ON VENTRAL MUSCLES OF NECK AND LOWER JAW

1. Name the principal muscles that are attached to the lower jaw. (Fig. 34, *A*)

2. Name the three large cartilages of the larynx on which several of these muscles are attached. (Figs. 34, *A* to *C*)

3. What is the principal difference between the cleidomastoid and sternomastoid muscles in the cat and man? (Fig. 34, *A* to *C*)

4. State the origin and insertion of each of the two principal cutaneous muscles of the cat. (Fig. 24)

5. What is the relationship of the position of the sternomastoid muscle to the external jugular vein? (Fig. 34, *B*)

6. Name a muscle that extends transversely between the lower jaws and also name a muscle in the region of the larynx (Fig. 34, *A* and *B*)

7. Name the salivary glands and state their relative positions to one another. (Fig. 34, *B*)

8. State the exact location of the large lymph glands that lie close to the salivary glands. (Fig. 34, *B*)

9. What two muscles lie parallel and ventral to most of the trachea? (Fig. 34, *A*)

10. Name four branchial muscles. (Fig. 34, A to C)

11. Name four brachial muscles. (Figs. 28 and 29)

12. Name the principal muscles used in chewing. (Fig. 34, A to C)

13. How do the sternomastoid and cleidomastoid muscles differ in the cat and in man? (Figs. 27 and 34, A)

14. What large vein is close to the surface in the neck? (Fig. 34, A and B)

15. Name two longitudinal muscles lying between the lower jaws. (Fig. 34, C)

16. What is the position of the thyroid gland in reference to the larynx and trachea? (Fig. 34, C)

17. How many sections make up the sternebrae? (Figs. 1 and 34, A; see mounted skeleton of the cat.)

18. Name the principal artery that carries the blood to the head. (Fig. 34, C)

19. Name three oblique muscles lying below the tongue and contributing to its movements. (Fig. 34, C)

20. Describe the shape and attachments of the scalenus muscle. (Fig. 34, A)

LEFT LATERAL VIEW OF MUSCLES OF LATERAL THORAX AND ABDOMINAL WALL (Fig. 35)

1. The **serratus posticus superior** may be identified as follows. Completely remove the upper portion of the latissimus dorsi muscle and reflect the trapezius and rhomboideus muscles as shown in Fig. 35. Find four or five rather indistinct myotomes above and posterior to the scapula, coming down from near the thoracic vertebrae and attaching to the ribs. Cut the common sheath covering them and with a dissecting needle determine the direction of the muscle fibers. This muscle was first named on man, where in the erect position it is truly above or superior to the following muscle, the serratus posticus inferior. These muscles help elevate the ribs.

2. The **serratus posticus inferior (serratus dorsalis caudalis)** is much like the preceding muscle. It is thin, lying caudad to the serratus posticus superior and median to the upper part of the latissimus dorsi. It arises by four or five fleshy heads, or myotomes, from the last four or five ribs. Passing dorsally the fibers unite to insert on the lumbar spinous processes and intervening interspinous ligaments. Bisect.

3. The **external intercostals** may be identified as follows. Pull the upper edge of the scapula away from the spinal column and with a needle determine the direction of the fibers of the external intercostals between the ribs immediately above the attachment of the serratus, anterior to the body wall. The origin is on the inferior margin of the superior ribs. The fibers run **caudad** and **ventrally** to insert on the anterior margins of the ribs. Numerous external intercostals are found in the outer portion of the intercostal spaces. They are the same in man. Their action is the protraction of the ribs.

4. The **internal intercostals** may be identified as follows. Disect off a small area of the thin external intercostal fibers between the adjacent **ribs** and observe the internal intercostal fibers extending **downward** and **forward.** These two layers of intercostals are believed to have originated from a common layer that extended more nearly parallel with the ribs. The action of the internal intercostals is the retraction of the ribs. The intercostals can be found almost anyplace between the ribs.

5. The fibers of the **external oblique (external abdominis oblique)**, which was mentioned previously, run posteriorly and ventrally. The muscle is large and thin, covering the lateral wall of the abdomen and part of the thorax. It arises from the last nine or ten ribs by numerous tendons, which are interwoven. These fibers expand out in a fanlike fashion with some caudal fibers inserted onto the cranial border of the pubis. The cranial fibers run downward into a median raphe, while median fibers join the **linea alba,** which is the median white line of the abdomen. The muscle is the same in man. The contracting action compresses the abdominal viscera from near the middle of the sternum to near the lumbar vertebrae. Bisect the external oblique at right angles to the fibers a distance of about six inches if not previously done and reflect as shown in Fig. 35.

6. The **internal oblique** is median to the external oblique and is tight against the transversus abdominis. It arises from the lumbar aponeurosis common to it and the external oblique, and by an aponeurosis it is united to the linea alba. Its fibers extend ventrally and slightly anteriorly, almost at right angles to fibers of the external oblique. The caudal fibers pass externally to the **rectus abdominis.** The muscle is the same in man. It acts as a compressor of the abdomen. Bisect through the muscle fiber area and reflect.

7. The **transversus abdominis** is the most internal of the abdominal muscles. It is thin and arises from cartilages of the false ribs, from transverse processes of the lumbar vertebrae, and from the ventral border of the ilium. Its fibers are almost parallel with those of the external oblique. A portion of the internal oblique is removed in the drawing to show the transverse abdominis. It acts as a constrictor of the abdomen. Under the transversus abdominis is the shiny transparent lining of the abdominal cavity, the **parietal peritoneum.**

Observe that in each of the layers of

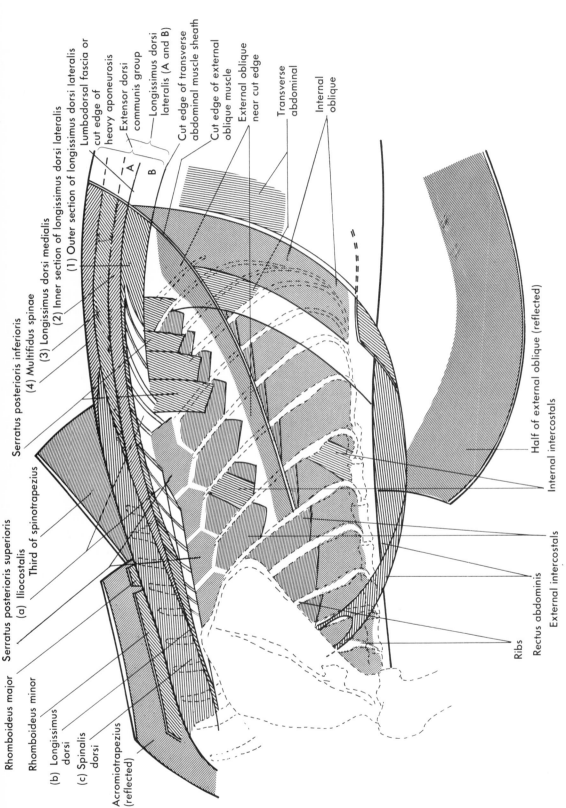

Rhomboideus major

Serratus posterioris superioris

Serratus posterioris inferioris

(a) Iliocostalis

Third of spinotrapezius

Rhomboideus minor

(4) Multifidus spinae

(3) Longissimus dorsi medialis

(2) Inner section of longissimus dorsi lateralis

(1) Outer section of longissimus dorsi lateralis

(b) Longissimus dorsi

(c) Spinalis dorsi

Acromiotrapezius (reflected)

Lumbodorsal fascia or cut edge of heavy aponeurosis

Extensor dorsi communis group

A

B

Longissimus dorsi lateralis (A and B)

Cut edge of transverse abdominal muscle sheath

Cut edge of external oblique muscle

External oblique near cut edge

Transverse abdominal

Internal oblique

Half of external oblique (reflected)

Internal intercostals

External intercostals

Rectus abdominis

Ribs

Fig. 35. Muscles of thorax and abdominal wall, superficial muscles displaced, left lateral view.

oblique muscles the fibers extend in a different direction. This arrangement is similar to the direction of the grain of wood fibers in plywood, which gives the abdominal wall greater strength for the amount of material involved. It is the same in man.

8. The **rectus abdominis** is about one-half inch wide, lying on each side of the midventral line, or linea alba, of the abdomen. This muscle extends from the pectoralis muscle posteriorly to the pubic symphysis. Dissect out the left rectus abdominis and determine its relationship to other muscles and their fascia, particularly the external and internal oblique. Where are the limits of the **rectus abdominis?** This muscle supports the abdominal wall, especially during pregnancy. Do not bisect.

The abdominal wall consists of the last four named flat layers of muscles, with the parietal peritoneum, connective tissue, and the skin. Fat is usually deposited in the connective tissue layers so that the fat layers and the lean meat, or muscle layers, alternate. This is true in all fat mammals, and in the pig, when the body wall is sliced, it is recognized as bacon. The small pieces of cartilage often found in the edge of a slice of bacon are sections of costal cartilages from the lower ends of ribs.

In appendectomies on man, the surgeon usually cuts through each layer of abdominal muscle, parallel to its muscle fibers. This permits firmer stitches to be taken in closing the wound, a more rapid recovery, and a stronger abdominal wall.

9. The **extensor dorsi communis** is a group of epaxial muscles along almost the entire spinal column. They do not differ from one another as much as those in other regions; hence, they are more difficult to identify. These muscles are lateral to the neural spines and dorsal to the transverse processes, mostly in the lumbar and thoracic regions. The larger muscles in these two regions may be identified rather satisfactorily, but the smaller muscles and those in the transition region from lumbar to thoracic are much more complicated and difficult to identify.

The **extensor dorsi communis** group of muscles consists of many subdivisions and is quite complicated. Only the main divisions will be considered here. In general it is divided into four long parts—1, 2, 3, and 4 of Fig. 35. Some of these extend forward through the lumbar and thoracic regions and into the neck. These are called the **longissimus dorsi communis.** Other parts are found only in the lumbar or in the thoracic region. For convenience we will consider the lumbar region first.

(a) The **extensor dorsi communis,** or the **sacrospinalis,** of the lumbar region may be identified as follows. Reflect the dorsal portions of the external and internal oblique muscles and their sheaths to the middorsal line of the lumbar region. This should uncover a heavy white sheath or **aponeurosis,** the **lumbodorsalis fascia.** Cut through this sheath close to the spines and peel it laterally to the point where it passes medially between the **inner** (*A*) and **outer** (*B*) longissimus dorsi lateralis muscles (Fig. 35). The less heavy sheath of the **transverse abdominis** muscle and sometimes the fascia of the **internal oblique** turn medially lateral to 1, *B* and separate it from the **hypaxial** or iliopsoas muscle, which is below and lateral to the transverse processes of the lumbar vertebrae. No. 2, *A* is the **inner section** of the **longissimus dorsi lateralis** and is separated from the next more lateral muscle, the **outer longissimus dorsi lateralis** (1, *B*), by the heavy **aponeurosis** mentioned previously. No. 3 is the **median longissimus dorsi,** and no. 4, nearest the neural spines, is the **multifidus spinae.**

Separate these four muscles from one another but do not bisect. These muscles vary in their relative sizes in different cats. The last three sections also extend to the vertebrae of the tail. These support the small of the back and bend the body from side to side. The muscles of the **lumbar region of the cow** are the **choicest** and **most expensive cuts of meat** in the meat market. From the ribs back to the ilium are the cuts known as the **club steak, T-bone steak, porterhouse steak,** and **sirloin steak.** In man these muscles are important in maintaining the erect position and in giving strength to the back. If you look at a **T-bone steak** that has been cut carefully, you can recognize the long bone, which is the **transverse process** of the lumbar vertebra, and the bony cross of the "T" consists of one-half of the **neural arch** and spine and one-half of the **body** of the vertebra or centrum.

(b) The **tensor dorsi communis** of the thoracic region may be identified as follows. Reflect the rhomboideus minor and major and the spinotrapezius. You will find three main longitudinal muscle areas in the dorsal part of the thorax. We shall consider these, beginning with the most lateral.

(1) The **iliocostals** (a) have fibers that extend anteroventrally and unite by many small, white tendons to the upper parts of various ribs above the **serratus posterior superior** and **inferior** muscles.

(2) The **longissimus dorsi communis** (b) is median and dorsal to the iliocostals. This muscle is a continuation of the same group seen in the lumbar region and may be traced in some specimens posteriorly, where the continuity is seen. However, it usually becomes quite complicated, and the dissection is seldom satisfactory. Trace this longissimus dorsi, or extensor dorsi, communis forward into the neck where it becomes closely associated with the **splenius.** The longissimus dorsi divides into many small units that are attached to the cervical vertebrae.

(3) The **spinalis dorsi** (c) is dorsal and median to the longissimus dorsi in the thoracic region. It extends longitudinally lateral to and against the neural spines. There are many more small muscles and subdivisions of the **extensor dorsi communis** group that connect various parts of many vertebrae. Thus they give support and strength to the spinal column. The distinctions between their origins and insertions are not clearly demarcated. Do not bisect. They are very much the same in man.

Definitions of many scientific terms are given in the back of the book.

REVIEW QUESTIONS ON MUSCLES OF ABDOMINAL WALL

1. Name the muscles of the lateral abdominal wall. (Fig. 35)

2. In what direction do the muscle fibers of each of the abdominal wall muscles extend? (Fig. 35)

3. What is the advantage in the way in which abdominal muscle fibers lie in reference to each other? (Fig. 35)

4. Name four muscles of the lateral thoracic wall that show myotome or myomere arrangement. (Fig. 35)

5. How is adipose tissue, or fat, arranged in reference to the abdominal wall muscles? (Fig. 35)

6. Define and give an example of a retroperitoneal organ. (See definition of terms.) (Figs. 48 and 51)

7. In what direction are the abdominal muscles cut in an operation to remove the appendix? Why? (Fig. 35)

8. What is the name of the innermost layer of the abdominal wall? (Fig. 47, B)

9. In what direction do the fibers of the intercostal muscles extend? (Fig. 35)

10. What is the linea alba and what is its significance? (See definition of terms.)

11. Name three muscles that show myotomes quite clearly. (Figs. 25 and 35)

12. What muscles lie lateral to the lumbar vertebrae? (Fig. 35)

13. What is meant by the term "aponeurosis"? (See definition of terms; Figs. 35 and 36)

14. What muscles may be seen in a slice of bacon? (Fig. 35)

15. Sometimes round, hard objects that cannot be chewed are found in bacon. What are they? (Fig. 35)

16. Name the four principal kinds of skeletal muscle in cat or man and state the characteristics of each.

17. Describe the peritoneum and state where it is found. (See definition of terms.)

18. What is another name for fat in an animal?

19. How do the long bones of the leg increase in length?

20. Where are the choicest and also the most expensive cuts in a beef animal located? (Fig. 35)

SUPERFICIAL MUSCLES OF LEFT HIP AND THIGH (Fig. 36)

Remove the fat and fascia from the anterior, median, and lateral surfaces of the thigh, being careful not to injure any muscles. If the cat is a male, the sperm ducts, with their arteries and veins, will be found embedded in the fat near the pubic symphysis (see Fig. 51). The sperm duct is a dense white cord and appears superficially somewhat like a large nerve. Dissect out the sperm duct on one side from the testis through the inguinal canal, where it passes through the lower abdominal wall. The male reproductive organs will be considered more fully later.

1. The **sartorius** is about one and one-half inches wide and lies on the anterior portion of the median side of the thigh. It often extends over the anterior surface and slightly to the lateral surface of the thigh. Compare this muscle as shown in Figs. 27, 36, and 42. Loosen the lateral edges from the knee to the ilium and pass a probe under it from its origin on the ilium to its insertion by ligaments on the patella and internal tuberosity of the tibia. It helps to pull the thigh toward the median line and also rotates it. It is the same in man. After bisecting and reflecting, the circumflex lateral artery and vein may be seen supplying its undersurface.

2. Before dissecting the **biceps femoris,** observe the **saphena parva vein** along the posterior surface of the calf of the leg (see Fig. 53). This vein turns under the lower end of the biceps femoris toward the back of the knee through the fat to join the **popliteal vein,** which may be seen later. A small **communicating branch** continues up the posterior surface of the thigh and connects with the **inferior gluteal vein** of the hip. If these veins are dilated with blood or are injected, you can see them easily. They are not shown in Fig. 36.

The biceps femoris is large and powerful, covering much of the lateral surface of the thigh. It is two or two and one-half inches wide throughout most of its length. Find the anterior edge about one inch posterior to the sartorius, extending from the ischium to the tibia. Its posterior edge is approximately in line with that of the thigh and inserts on the upper half of the tibia. Find the posterior edge and pass a probe under it to its anterior edge. Loosen a small area, bisect the biceps femoris near its center, and reflect each of the ends completely, as shown in the illustration (Fig. 36). Much fat is usually deposited under its lower end. Pull out this fat with your fingers and expose the large **sciatic nerve,** which branches into the lateral **peroneus communis** and the median **tibial nerve.** The area that this fat occupies is the popliteal space, and through it the popliteal vein, previously mentioned, and artery pass. There is usually a lymph gland embedded within the fat.

3. The **tenuissimus** is often one-half centimeter wide and is sometimes difficult to locate. It is usually found on the median side of the biceps femoris when reflected but extends almost parallel to the sciatic nerve. It arises from the transverse process of the second caudal vertebra. It extends along the inner posterior edge of the biceps femoris, with which it eventually fuses. It is absent in man.

4. The **caudofemoralis** is at the upper anterior edge of the biceps femoris and sometimes is attached to it. Its origin is on the transverse processes of the second and third caudal vertebrae. The upper half is muscular, whereas the lower half is simply the sheath of fascia, which is thin and small, parallel with and lateral to the femur. It is inserted into the middle of the lateral border of the patella. It is absent in man. It acts as an abductor of the thigh and a flexor of the shank. Bisect through its upper muscular portion on the level with the head of the femur. After bisecting you can see the base of the tenuissimus muscle better. Sometimes the caudofemoralis is reflected with the biceps femoris.

5. The **tensor fasciae latae** is a very peculiar muscle, thick and wide at its upper extremity but reduced to heavy **fascia,** or **aponeurosis,** throughout its lower two-thirds and merges with the aponeurosis of the caudofemoralis. Its origin is on the anterior end of the ilium and adjacent fascia, covering the lateral anterior half of

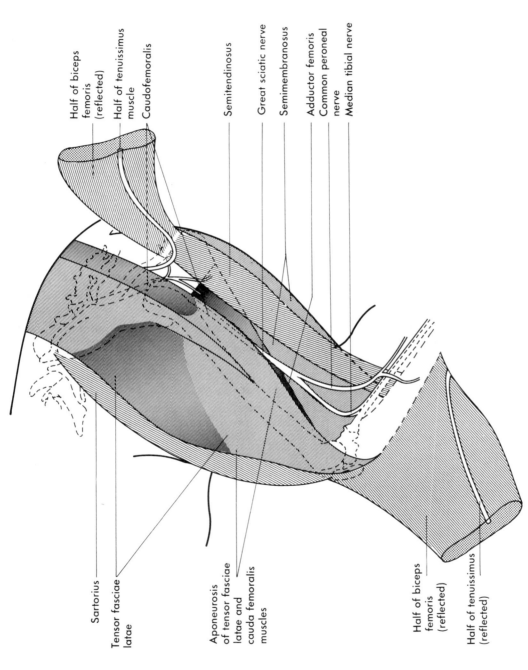

Sartorius

Tensor fasciae latae

Aponeurosis of tensor fasciae latae and cauda femoralis muscles

Half of biceps femoris (reflected)

Half of tenuissimus (reflected)

Half of biceps femoris (reflected)

Half of tenuissimus muscle

Caudofemoralis

Semitendinosus

Great sciatic nerve

Semimembranosus

Adductor femoris

Common peroneal nerve

Median tibial nerve

Fig. 36. Superficial muscles of hip and thigh, left lateral view.

74

the thigh, inserting by long, broad fascia to the external surface of the femur and on the tibia. It is much reduced in man (see Fig. 37). Locate the head of the femur and its entire extent by means of a dissecting needle. Cut the fascia of the extensor fasciae latae where it joins the entire lateral surface of the femur. Pass a probe under this fascia and the muscular portion of this muscle and bisect through its thickest part. Separate the upper portion of the tensor fasciae latae from the head of the femur and along the lower edge of the ilium.

Muscles are surrounded by fascia that sometimes thickens into a **heavy aponeurosis,** as is the case of the lower part of the tensor fasciae latae. The real muscle fibers have migrated or disappeared from this area, leaving only this heavy sheath. This has probably resulted in part from the fact that the area is struck by more objects when the animal runs.

When a leg of lamb is purchased at the market, usually the butcher peels and cuts off this heavy fascia, or aponeurosis, and discards it **after** it has been weighed. See Fig. 37 for the tensor fasciae latae of man.

6. The **semitendinosus** muscle is not half tendon, as the name implies, but is muscular except near its insertion. It lies median and posterior to the biceps femoris along the posterior portion of the thigh, is nearly uniform, and is about the size of a human finger. It arises from the tuberosity of the ischium and inserts on the median side of the tibia. It helps to bend the shank. Bisect and reflect.

7. The name of the **semimembranosus** is definitely misleading, since the muscle is large and muscular in the cat (see Fig. 37). It lies median and anterior to the semitendinosus and the lower part of the **sciatic nerve.** This muscle must be observed from the median surface of the thigh before it can be bisected properly. Identify the conspicuous saphena magna vein passing diagonally across the lower part of the thigh and calf of the leg. Loosen the thin, broad gracilis muscle, bisect, and reflect it to expose the median side of the semimembranosus, as shown in Fig. 42. The semimembranosus muscle usually appears folded

upon itself with two layers along its anterior edge and one along its posterior edge. Its anterior edge lies close to the adductor femoris muscle. The insertion is along the distal posterior portion of the femur. It is a powerful muscle that helps to draw the leg backward.

The biceps femoris, semitendinosus, and the semimembranosus muscles are known as the "hamstring" muscles.

8. The **adductor femoris** (adductor magnus of man) (Fig. 37) lies immediately anterior to the semimembranosus, mostly between it and the femur. This muscle does not really belong to the superficial group; however, it is closely associated with the previously named muscles. On its lateral surface its fibers usually extend obliquely to the semimembranosus, whereas on its median surface they are almost parallel to it. The adductor femoris arises on the ischium and pubic symphysis and passes downward and anteriorly to be inserted along most of the entire length of the femur. It is powerful, although its fibers are not closely bound together. It helps to pull the femur back in jumping or walking.

Thigh muscles of a beef animal constitute "round steaks."

LEFT LATERAL VIEW OF SMALLER AND DEEPER MUSCLES OF LEFT HIP (Figs. 38 to 41)

1. The **gluteus maximus** (Fig. 38) was first named on man, where it is the largest of the three glutei muscles and forms the principal cushion when he sits (Fig. 37), but in the cat the gluteus medius is the largest and lies under the anterior edge of the upper end of the caudofemoralis. The gluteus maximus arises from the sacrum and the first two caudal vertebrae and extends laterally over the innominate bone and inserts below the greater trochanter of the femur. It is about one-half inch wide and two inches long in a medium-sized cat. It is an abductor muscle, since it helps to pull the thigh away from the median plane of the animal's body. Loosen its edges, bisect, and reflect. This will expose more of the **sciatic nerve.**

2. The **gluteus medius** (Fig. 38) is the

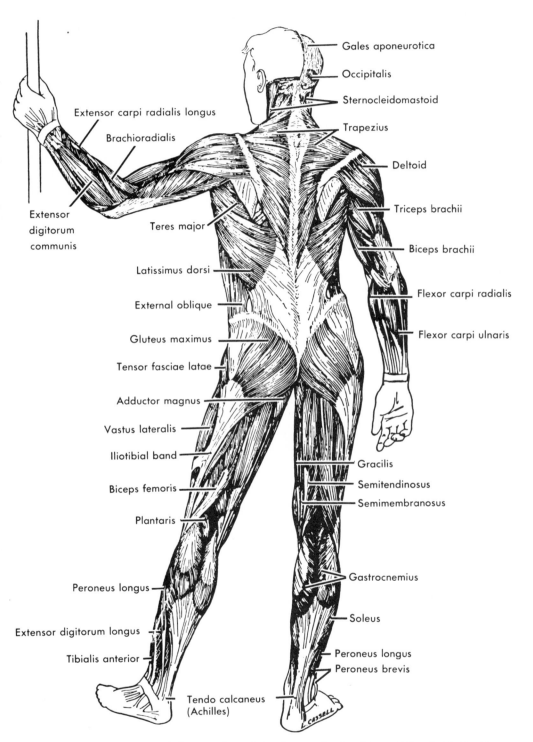

Gales aponeurotica

Occipitalis

Sternocleidomastoid

Trapezius

Deltoid

Triceps brachii

Biceps brachii

Flexor carpi radialis

Flexor carpi ulnaris

Extensor carpi radialis longus

Brachioradialis

Extensor digitorum communis

Teres major

Latissimus dorsi

External oblique

Gluteus maximus

Tensor fasciae latae

Adductor magnus

Vastus lateralis

Iliotibial band

Biceps femoris

Plantaris

Gracilis

Semitendinosus

Semimembranosus

Gastrocnemius

Soleus

Peroneus longus

Peroneus longus

Peroneus brevis

Extensor digitorum longus

Tibialis anterior

Tendo calcaneus (Achilles)

Fig. 37. Posterior view of the muscles of the human body. (From Millard, N. D., King, B. G., and Showers, M. J.: Human anatomy and physiology, Philadelphia, 1956, W. B. Saunders Co.)

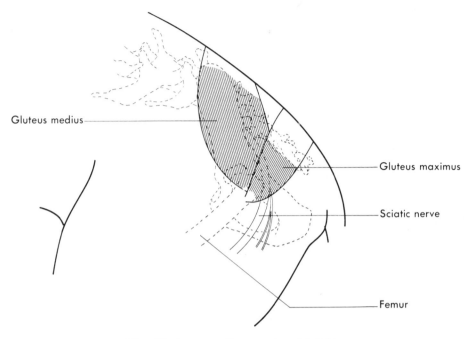

Gluteus medius

Gluteus maximus

Sciatic nerve

Femur

Fig. 38. Some smaller muscles of left hip.

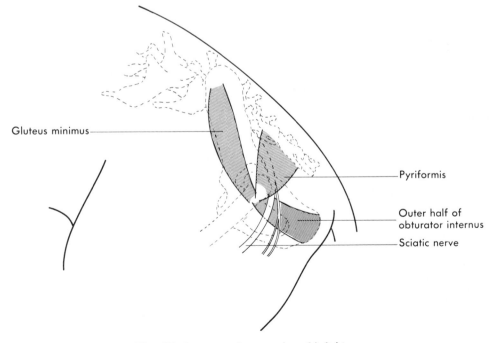

Gluteus minimus

Pyriformis

Outer half of
obturator internus

Sciatic nerve

Fig. 39. Some smaller muscles of left hip.

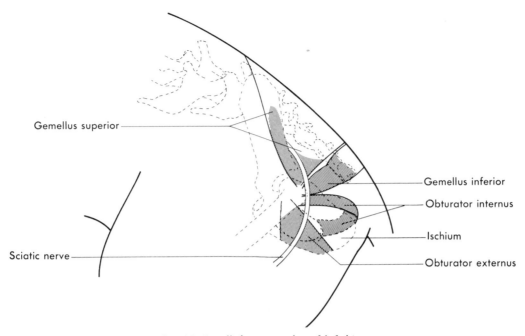

Fig. 40. Small deep muscles of left hip.

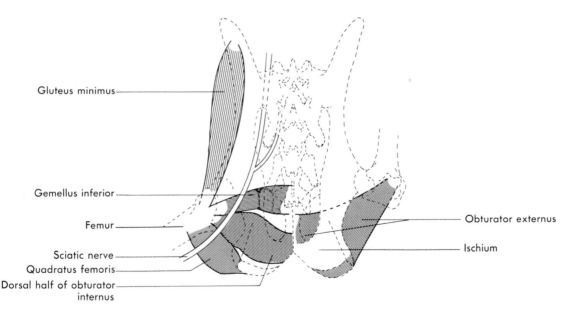

Fig. 41. Small deep muscles of the pelvis, dorsal view.

largest of the gluteal muscles in the cat. It arises on the anterior end of the ilium and passes posteriorly and laterally dorsal to the ilium and inserts on the greater trochanter of the femur. It is twice the size of the gluteus maximus. If the upper end of the tensor fasciae latae was properly reflected, the lateral edge of the gluteus medius is already exposed. If not, dissect off the fascia covering the gluteus medius. Lift up the thick lateral edge from the gluteus minimus, which usually has a white sheath, and insert a probe between them close to the femur, which should be pushed up in order to make this procedure easier. Do not mutilate the underlying muscles. It is often difficult to bisect and reflect the gluteus medius because of its thickness and the presence of the extensor dorsi communis muscle in the sacral region. If, after bisecting, the portion close to the femur separates easily into two parts and the lower part has many white fibers in contact with the sciatic nerve, then it is quite certain that the pyriformis has been bisected also.

3. The **pyriformis** lies below portions of the gluteus maximus and gluteus medius. It may have been bisected with the latter because the lower portions are almost merged with one another. If the pyriformis has been bisected and reflected with the gluteus medius, the base of the sciatic nerve can be traced over the ilium between it and the sacrum. The pyriformis may be identified by the white, shiny tendon that joins the femur and by its triangular shape. It arises from the ventrolateral surface of the sacrum and the first few caudal vertebrae, passes dorsal to the **sciatic nerve,** and inserts on the greater trochanter of the femur. Bisect it if that has not been done. It helps to draw and hold the head of the femur in the acetabulum. It is much the same in man. This muscle is shown in Fig. 39.

4. The **gluteus minimus** is under the lateral edge of the gluteus medius. It is cylindrical and almost cigar shaped. It arises on the lateral and dorsal surfaces of the ilium and inserts on the greater trochanter of the femur. It is much the same in man, since it helps to rotate the femur. Do not bisect the gluteus minimus. This muscle is shown in Figs. 39 and 41.

5. The **obturator internus** may be identified as follows. Bisect the **sciatic nerve** near the head of the femur and pull the proximal portion up against the reflected pyriformis and gluteus medius. Dissect off the fascia and fat dorsal and median to the posterior end of the ischium and push the base of the tail away from the ischium. The obturator internus is horse-shoe shaped, as shown in Fig. 40, and passes over the posterior inner surface of the ischium, so only the dorsal half is seen in Figs. 39 and 41. The origin is on the lower median portion of the ischium close to the pubis. It passes dorsalward between the

base of the tail and ischium and curves over the ischium and under the sciatic nerve to insert on the greater trochanter of the femur. It is usually about one-half inch wide and helps to pull the head of the femur medially and posteriorly. Loosen the dorsal half but do not bisect.

6. The **gemellus inferior** lies anterior to the dorsal half of the obturator internus, and the two unite in a common flat, white tendon and insert on the femur. The origin is on the second or third caudal vertebra from which the muscle passes over the innominate bone, where some of the fibers also arise, and continues laterally to merge with the insertion of the obturator internus. It is about one centimeter wide and is slightly constricted as it passes over the innominate bone. Loosen the edges but do not bisect. If possible, obtain some modeling clay and model these small muscles on the mounted cat's skeleton to get a definite idea of their relationships. Most of these small muscles are not shown in Figs. 27 and 37.

7. The **gemellus superior** lies immediately anterior to the gemellus inferior. Its lateral surface is against the inner side of the gluteus minimus and is below the base of the **sciatic nerve.** It arises on the crest of the ilium and inserts on the head of the femur. Separate its edges from the previously named muscles but do not bisect. These smaller muscles of the hip help to hold the head of the femur in its socket, the acetabulum. This muscle is shown in Fig. 40.

8. The **quadratus femoris** lies immediately dorsal and lateral to the adductor femoris and lateral to the inner end of the obturator internus. Bisect the adductor femoris in a plane extending from the center of the ventral edge dorsalward to the insertion of its upper edge near the head of the femur. Pull the femur forward and reflect both ends of the adductor femoris. The lateral surface of the quadratus is now exposed. This muscle is four sided, almost a cube, in relation to its origin and insertion, which are on the ischium and greater trochanter, respectively. It is an extensor and rotator of the thigh. It is the same in man.

Do not bisect. This muscle is shown in Fig. 41.

9. The **obturator externus** lies below the quadratus femoris and ischium, but median to the posterior portion of the adductor femoris. Pull the posterior portion of the adductor femoris ventralward to expose the lateral triangular surface of the obturator externus. It arises from the lower posterior part of the ischium and the pubis near the symphysis. Its fibers extend dorso-laterally and forward to insert on the femur lateral and distal to the lesser trochanter. Do not bisect. Pull the femur forward and outward to see the triangular posterior surface of the adductor longus and the femoral artery and vein passing almost parallel to its lower edge. This muscle is shown in Figs. 40 and 41. The branches of the greater **sciatic nerve** are more completely shown in Fig. 72.

MEDIAN VIEW OF MEDIAN AND DEEPER MUSCLES OF LEFT THIGH (Fig. 42)

1. The **sartorius** has been considered in a previous group because it appears on the lateral surface and on the anterior half of the median surface. It has been bisected, but in Fig. 42 it is shown intact. In man it is the longest muscle in the body, since it arises on the outer anterior crest of the ilium and passes obliquely across the front of the thigh to the median side of the knee and attaches by an aponeurosis to the tibia. This can be seen in Fig. 27 (the anterior view of man's muscles).

Anterior to the femur and partially covered by the sartorius, as shown in Fig. 42, is the **vastus medialis** or **internus**. It is close against the femur and arises from it and the ilium. The **rectus femoris** is anterior and lateral to the vastus internus and arises entirely from the ilium. The circumflex artery passes between these two muscles (see Figs. 42 and 58). Still farther forward and arising from the ilium is the **tensor fasciae latae,** of which only a portion is shown in Fig. 42 and may be completely covered in this view by the sartorius.

2. The **gracilis** was bisected in order to see the median sides of the **semitendinosus**

and **semimembranosus,** hence it is shown reflected in Fig. 42. It is broad and thin, covering the posterior portion of the inner or median surface of the thigh. In several respects it seems comparable with the epitrochlean of the forelimb. The gracilis arises near the **symphysis pubis** and inserts on the inner side of the proximal side of the tibia. Part of the fascia joins with that of the tensor fasciae latae. It is an adductor of the thigh. It is the same in man.

3. The **rectus** or **adductor femoris** is a large muscle and arises from the rami of the pubis and ischium and inserts on the median inner surface of the femur. It lies along the anterior edge of the semimembranosus and inserts on about the middle third of the shaft of the femur. It corresponds with the adductor magnus, adductor longus, and adductor brevis of man. Its action is to extend the thigh after it has been drawn forward. The anterior edge of the adductor femoris may separate off and appear as an additional muscle.

4. The **adductor longus** is much smaller than the adductor femoris and is only about one inch long. It lies in contact with the anterior proximal surface of the adductor femoris. It extends from the pubic bone to the distal end of the upper third of the femur. Do not bisect.

5. The **pectineus** is still smaller than the adductor longus and lies anterior to it and under the anterior proximal edge of the gracilis. It arises on the pubis and inserts on the upper end of the femur.

6. The **iliopsoas** is a long and cylindrical muscle and lies along the inner surface of the dorsal body wall in the lumbar region. It arises from the undersides of the transverse processes of the last two thoracic and the lumbar vertebrae. It is a hypaxial muscle, being below the transverse processes, in distinction to the extensor dorsi communis group, which is epaxial, or above, the transverse processes. The iliopsoas passes posteriorly through the body wall dorsal to the inguinal region but ventral to the **ilium.** It may be partially uncovered as it inserts on the lesser trochanter of the femur. Do not bisect. In man there are three muscles corresponding to this one in

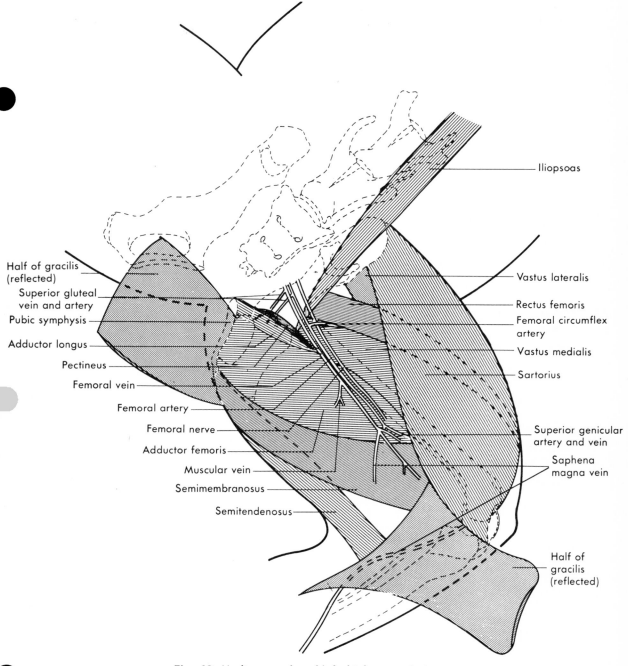

Fig. 42. Median muscles of left thigh, ventral view.

Iliopsoas

Half of gracilis (reflected)

Superior gluteal vein and artery

Pubic symphysis

Adductor longus

Pectineus

Femoral vein

Femoral artery

Femoral nerve

Adductor femoris

Muscular vein

Semimembranosus

Semitendenosus

Vastus lateralis

Rectus femoris

Femoral circumflex artery

Vastus medialis

Sartorius

Superior genicular artery and vein

Saphena magna vein

Half of gracilis (reflected)

the cat: the iliacus, psoas major, and psoas minor.

The femoral, or Scarpa's, triangle is an important area on the median surface of the thigh. It is bounded by the proximal half of the posterior edge of the sartorius and a line along the femur where the adductor femoris and adductor longus attach to the femur. The third side of the triangle is the lateral edge of the ilium. Extending across this triangle are the following structures: (a) The **external iliac**, or **femoral, artery** is usually injected with red latex. It gives off the circumflex to the deep muscles that arise on the ilium and upper part of the femur. (b) The **femoral**, or **external iliac, vein** is usually larger than the artery and dark because of the blue injecting material or the coagulated blood. It receives the **deep femoral vein** from under the proximal end of the gracilis and adductor femoris muscles. This vein is parallel with an artery of the same name (not shown in Fig. 42—see Fig. 53). At about the middle of the thigh one or more **muscular veins** enter the femoral from the adductor femoris and semimembranosus muscles. Color these blood vessels red or blue according to the

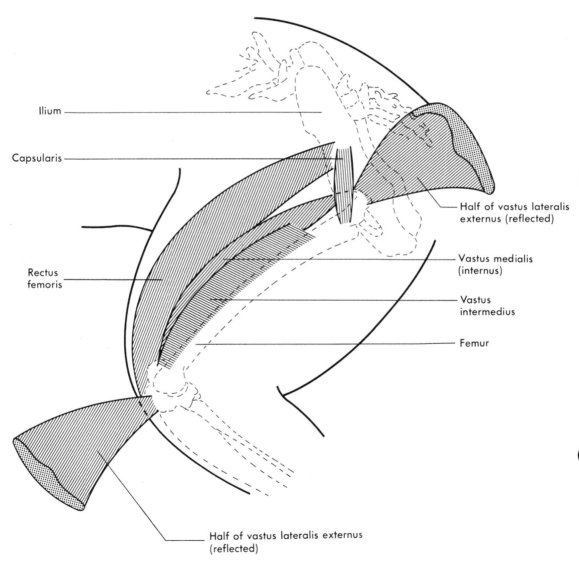

Ilium

Capsularis

Rectus femoris

Half of vastus lateralis externus (reflected)

Vastus medialis (internus)

Vastus intermedius

Femur

Half of vastus lateralis externus (reflected)

Fig. 43. Deep quadratus muscles of thigh, left lateral view.

purity of the blood. (c) The **femoral nerve** is usually anterior or dorsal to the blood vessels at its base and farther out gives off branches to the superficial muscles of the thigh and shank. More details will be given on these blood vessels and nerves later.

DEEP MUSCLES OF ANTERIOR PORTION OF LEFT THIGH (Fig. 43)

The **quadriceps femoris** (quadriceps extensor group) consists of four muscles that have separate origins but insert on the tibia by the common tendon of the patella.

1. The **vastus lateralis**, or **externus**, is partially under the tensor fasciae latae and is posterior to the sartorius. It is the largest of the group and the most external of the four. It arises on the outer surface of the shaft of the femur and on the greater trochanter. Passing down, it joins with other muscles to insert on the lateral surface of the patella in the so-called patella tendon. It is the same in man. It acts as an extensor of the shank. Separate it from the two underlying muscles, beginning at its upper anterior surface. In addition, cut it loose along its posterior edge from the femur. Bisect and reflect as shown in Fig. 43.

2. The **rectus femoris** is the most anterior of the four muscles, is uniform in size, and lies between the vastus externus and sartorius. It arises from the **ilium** above the acetabulum. It passes caudad to join the vastus lateralis and inserts in common with it in the patella tendon. It is the same in man. It acts as an extensor of the shank. Bisect.

3. The **vastus internus**, or **medialis**, lies posterior and median to the rectus femoris and is covered medially by the sartorius. The sheath or fascia of the tensor fasciae latae is attached to it. Its origin is from the inner and anterior surface of the proximal end of the femur. It inserts on the medial margin of the patella tendon. It is the same in man. It acts as an extensor of the shank. Do not bisect.

4. The **vastus intermedius** is the smallest of the four muscles. It arises along the anterior and lateral surfaces of the femur, to which it adheres closely. It is median to the vastus lateralis and soon merges with the vastus internus, and the two often appear as one muscle. To expose this muscle, reflect muscles one, two, and three. It is the same in man. It acts as an extensor of the shank. Do not bisect.

5. The **capsularis**, or accessory gluteus minimus, is closely associated with the quadriceps femoris group. It arises on the outer posterior surface of the ilium and passes posteriorly between the origins of the rectus femoris and the vastus lateralis to insert on the lateral surface of the femur above the vastus intermedius. It is small, only about one inch long, anterior to and below the head of the femur. It helps to rotate the thigh and pull it forward.

The muscles of the thigh of a beef animal constitute the **round steak** at the meat market.

REVIEW QUESTIONS ON MUSCLES OF HIP AND THIGH

1. Name five superficial muscles of the hip and thigh of the cat and of man. (Figs. 36, 37, and 42)

2. Name five small, deep muscles of the hip. (Figs. 38, 39, 40, and 41)

3. Describe the structure of the tensor fasciae latae muscle. (Fig. 36)

4. What two narrow and almost parallel structures lie median to the biceps femoris muscle? (Fig. 36)

5. What are the relationships of the caudofemoralis muscle to the tensor fasciae latae and biceps femoris? (Fig. 36)

6. What are the names of the two large muscles on the median surface of the thigh? (Fig. 42)

7. State the principal differences of the glutei maximus muscles of cat and man. (Figs. 37 and 38)

8. Compare the sartorius muscles of the cat and man. (Figs. 27, 36, and 42)

9. Name the small muscles that are inserted on the proximal end of the femur. (Figs. 38, 39, 40, and 41)

10. Name the three gluteal muscles. (Figs. 38 and 39)

11. Which muscles are known as the "hamstring" muscles? (Fig. 42)

12. What muscle curves over the inner and outer surfaces of the ischium? (Figs. 40 and 41)

13. What are the two main divisions of the great sciatic nerve? (Fig. 36)

14. Where is Scarpa's triangle and what are its boundaries? (Fig. 42)

15. What ventral thigh muscles originate on the pubic bone? (Fig. 42)

16. What long, slender muscle lies along the median side of biceps femoris? (Fig. 36)

17. Describe the tensor fasciae latae muscle. (Fig. 36)

18. What is the advantage of having heavy fascia (aponeurosis) on the outside rather than on the inside of the thigh? (Use your judgment.)

19. Heavy fascia, or aponeurosis, of the thigh represents a modified part of what muscle? (Fig. 36)

20. Why do the names of the glutei muscles seem inappropriate?

POSTERIOR MUSCLES OF LEFT SHANK, OR CALF (Fig. 44)

Reflect the lower portion of the biceps femoris, including its broad sheath on the outer surface of the shank, and the semitendinosus and semimembranosus completely in order to see the following structures. The **saphena parva vein,** mentioned in connection with the thigh, comes up the posterior surface of the shank to join the **popliteal vein** behind the knee joint (see Fig. 53). A **communicating branch** of the **saphena parva** extends up the posterior surface of the thigh and connects with the **gluteus inferior** of the hip. Often these veins are not injected nor dilated with coagulated blood and hence are not easily seen.

1. The **plantaris muscle** arises from under the anterior edge of the biceps on the patella and passes across the lateral side of the knee and down between the two heads, inner and outer, of the gastrocnemius, merging with them. These help form the **tendon of calcaneus,** or **tendon of Achilles,** and insert on the **calcaneus,** or heel bone, at the hock. Loosen the edges of the plantaris lateral to the knee until it merges with the gastrocnemius. The **tibial branch of the sciatic nerve** passes between the plantaris and the inner head of the gastrocnemius. Separate the plantaris from the inner head and bisect the outer head where the two merge with one another. Sometimes the lower portion of the inner head can be separated also from the plantaris. The **femoral artery** and **vein** pass near the femur.

2. The **gastrocnemius** is the largest muscle in the lower portion of the leg. It has two heads, sometimes called the caput mediale and the caput laterale, one on either side of the plantaris. These two heads

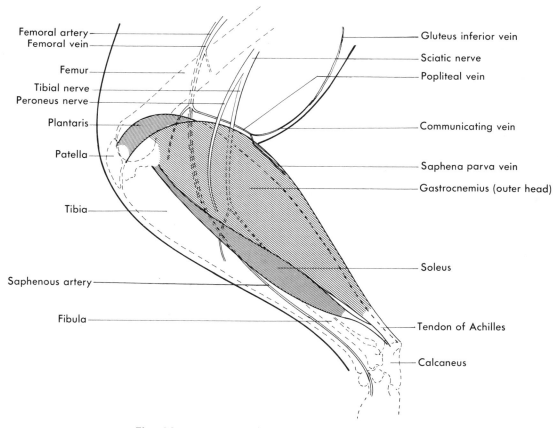

Fig. 44. Posterior muscles of left shank, lateral view.

merge with the plantaris, usually throughout their lower two-thirds. The **peroneal branch of the sciatic nerve** passes lateral to the lateral head of the gastrocnemius and penetrates its lateral anterior edge.

3. The **soleus** arises anterior to the lateral head of the gastrocnemius from the lateral surface of the head of the fibula. It extends median to the lateral head of the gastrocnemius, and one-third or more of the muscle is exposed laterally before it joins the lateral surface of the gastrocnemius tendon to form the tendon of Achilles. The plantaris, gastrocnemius, and the soleus form most of the **calf of the leg.**

ANTERIOR AND DEEP MUSCLES OF LEFT SHANK (Figs. 44 and 45)

Remove two or three layers of the heavy fascia covering the lateral and anterior surfaces of the shank. Consider the lateral view of the left hind leg and proceed from the anterior to the posterior.

1. The **tibialis anterior** may be identified as follows. The sharp anterior edge of the tibia is known as the shinbone. Locate this sharp-edged bone on the cat and on yourself. This muscle lies immediately lateral to the tibia and occupies about three-fourths of the space between the tibia and fibula. The origin is on the upper anterolateral surface of the tibia and the shaft and head of the fibula. It passes distally down the anterolateral surface of the tibia and inserts on the outer surface of the first metatarsal. Separate the tibialis anterior from the extensor digitorum longus, which lies posterior to it. Insert a probe under the tibialis and bisect below the center. It is triangular in cross section and usually is much heavier near the proximal end.

2. The **extensor digitorum longus** lies

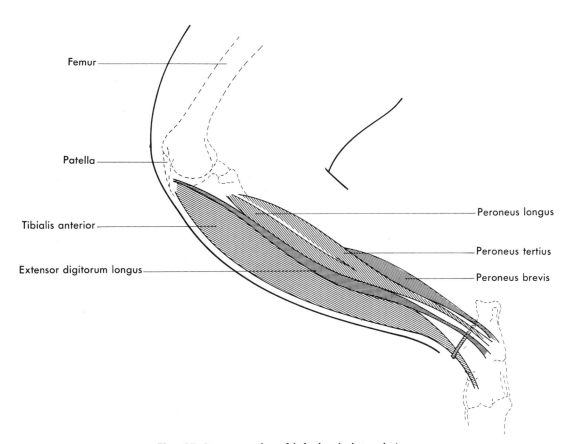

Fig. 45. Deep muscles of left shank, lateral view.

posterior to the tibialis anterior. Its proximal end is almost completely encased by the tibialis anterior. Medially and distally from the center of the leg its lateral surface is exposed to the superficial fascia, whereas its anterior and median surfaces are still bordered by the tibialis anterior. It originates on the lateral epicondyle of the femur and extends along the anterior side of the fibula. With the tibialis anterior it passes under the **annular, or transverse, ligament** on the outside of the hock. Do not bisect. Compare Figs. 44 and 45 with Fig. 37.

3. The **peroneus longus** is a slender, uniformly shaped, superficial muscle posterior to the extensor digitorum longus. It originates on the head and lateral surface of the fibula, and it inserts on the metatarsals. It acts as a flexor of the foot, as in man. The inner surface lies above the two following muscles. Do not bisect.

4. The **peroneus tertius** is a long, slender muscle lying directly beneath the peroneus longus and is usually smaller. It originates by fleshy fibers from the second quarter of the lateral surface of the fibula and ends in a thin, shiny tendon that passes through the groove of the lateral malleolus of the fibula. The proximal end is covered by the peroneus longus and distally is covered by superficial fascia and lies posterior to the peroneus longus.

5. The **peroneus brevis** is a short, thick muscle lying beneath the other peronei, originating by fleshy fibers from the distal half of the fibula under the upper end of the soleus. It adheres to and extends along the lateral part of the fibula and ends by passing through the groove on the ventral border of the lateral malleolus with the peroneus tertius. The lateral surface is covered by the peroneus longus, peroneus tertius, and superficial fascia; the inner surface is covered by the fibula. Do not loosen from the fibula nor bisect.

DEEPER POSTERIOR MUSCLES OF LEFT SHANK (Fig. 46, A and B)

Reflect the **gastrocnemius, plantaris,** and **soleus** muscles as shown in the posterior view in Fig. 46 so that you can get a definite posterior view of the deeper muscles.

The **peroneus longus, peroneus tertius,** and **peroneus brevis** are shown in the left portion of this drawing also. The following muscles will be considered in order, beginning on the upper median surface and proceeding laterally.

1. The **popliteus** is a short, broad, tapering, triangular muscle arising on the lateral epicondyle of the femur almost beneath the lateral head of the gastrocnemius. It extends over the lateral articulate facet on the proximal end of the tibia and inserts on the medial, proximal, and upper end of the medial portion of the tibia. The lateral surface is medial to the gastrocnemius and plantaris and the insertion of the semitendinosus. Its action rotates the leg. See Fig. 46, B for the median view of those same muscles.

2. The **flexor digitorum longus** is a long, tapering muscle lying lateral to the distal edge of the popliteus and extending from its origin on the lateral surface of the fibula to a fine tendon. It originates on the proximal, ventral surface of the tibia, extends down the median surface of the tibia, receiving fibers therefrom, and ends in a thin, shiny tendon that passes over the ventral groove on the distal end of the fibula. It is bordered medially by the medial head of the gastrocnemius and superficial fascia.

3. The **tibialis posterior** is a long, thin, flat muscle beneath and lateral to the flexor digitorum longus and between it and the flexor hallucis longus. It originates on the medial surface of the head of the fibula and ventral surface of the tibia, extending as a thin, flat muscle to the middle of the fibula, where it merges with a thin, flat, shiny tendon and inserts on the tarsals.

4. The **flexor hallucis longus** is a long, heavy muscle lateral to the tibialis posterior and connected to the posterior border of the tibia by the fleshy fibers from the anterior end to within one to three centimeters of the distal end. It is also attached to the proximal posterior end of the fibula by fleshy fibers. It passes down the posterior surface of the leg to the ankle as a uniform, broad muscle anterior to the **tibial nerve.**

In the median view in Fig. 46, B the

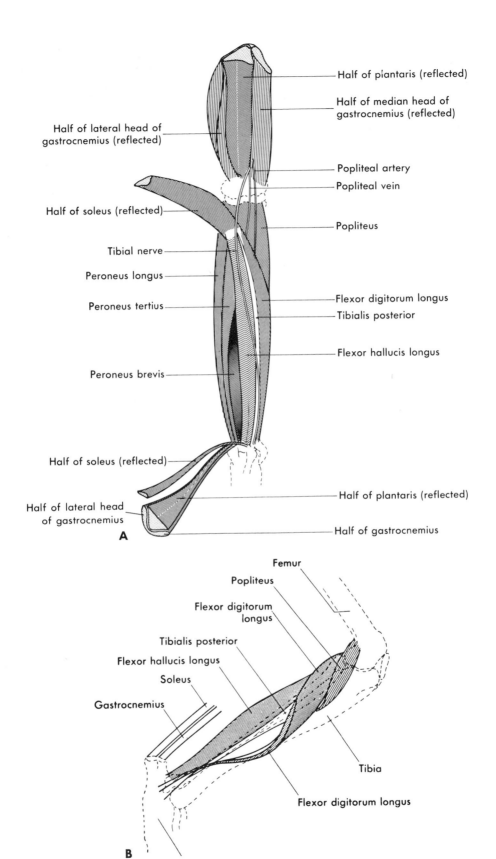

Half of plantaris (reflected)

Half of median head of gastrocnemius (reflected)

Half of lateral head of gastrocnemius (reflected)

Popliteal artery

Popliteal vein

Half of soleus (reflected)

Popliteus

Tibial nerve

Peroneus longus

Peroneus tertius

Flexor digitorum longus

Tibialis posterior

Flexor hallucis longus

Peroneus brevis

Half of soleus (reflected)

Half of plantaris (reflected)

Half of lateral head of gastrocnemius

Half of gastrocnemius

A

Femur

Popliteus

Flexor digitorum longus

Tibialis posterior

Flexor hallucis longus

Soleus

Gastrocnemius

Tibia

Flexor digitorum longus

B

Fig. 46. A, Posterior and **B,** median views of deep muscles of left shank.

four muscles just discussed are shown. The flexor digitorum longus is pulled forward to better expose the tibialis posterior.

The **tibial nerve** passes between the median head of the gastrocnemius and plantaris muscles and continues between the tibialis and the flexor hallucis muscles, sending branches to the lower shank and foot. The **popliteal artery,** which is a continuation of the femoral, passes through the popliteal space, follows the tibial nerve, and then passes between the popliteal and flexor digitorum longus muscles. It continues between the tibia and fibula, where it is known as the anterior tibial artery. The **popliteal vein** lies close to the popliteal artery and receives the saphena parva vein and the posterior tibial.

At the place where the same muscle is shown in both drawings in Fig. 46, *A* and *B* it should be given the same specific color in both, and any other muscle shown twice should likewise be given a different specific color but the same for the same muscle, etc. In this manner the two views of the same muscle can be recognized more easily.

REVIEW QUESTIONS ON MUSCLES OF SHANK

1. What muscles constitute the calf of the leg? (Fig. 44)

2. Describe the general form of the gastrocnemius muscle. (Fig. 44)

3. What muscles contribute to the tendon of Achilles? (Fig. 44)

4. Name three kinds of connective tissue associated with muscles.

5. What nerves supply most of the muscles of the calf of the leg? (Figs. 44 and 46, A)

6. What is the relation of the tendon of Achilles to the heel of man? (Figs. 1, 2, and 37)

7. What is the main function of the muscles of the calf of the leg? (Use your own judgment to answer.)

8. What artery and vein pass down the leg in back of the knee? (Figs. 46, 53)

9. What is an aponeurosis and where may it be found in the cat? (Figs. 35 and 36)

10. What bones support the shank muscles? (Figs. 1 and 2)

11. What bone is intermediate between the femur and the bones of the shank? (Figs. 1 and 2)

12. What is another name for the shinbone?

13. What are the lateral limits of Scarpa's triangle?

14. Name the two parts of the gastrocnemius muscle. (Figs. 37 and 46, A)

15. What muscle lies between the two parts of the gastrocnemius and merges with them? (Fig. 46, A)

16. From what part of a beef animal are round steaks cut?

17. What is the principal difference in the trapezius muscles of the cat and man? (Figs. 24 and 37)

18. Name three muscles of the thoracic wall which show the myomeres. (Figs. 27 and 35)

19. Why is there a relatively greater strain on the heart of man than on a cat when both are standing?

20. Do you think there is a difference in the demand on muscles in an animal whose body is horizontal and one in an erect position? (Use your own judgment to answer.)

SOME DIFFERENCES IN MUSCLES OF CAT AND MAN

Many muscles of man have apparently become modified largely because of the erect position of his body.

1. The clavotrapezius, acromiotrapezius, and spinotrapezius muscles in the cat are merged into one muscle in man.

2. The clavobrachialis, continuous with the clavotrapezius on the upper arm of the cat, is absent in man.

3. The acromiodeltoid and spinodeltoid muscles of the cat are merged into one deltoid muscle in man.

4. The epitrochlean, tenuissimus, cutaneous maximus, occipitoscapularis, and levator scapula ventralis muscles present in the cat are absent in man.

5. The sternomastoids and cleidomastoids are separate in the cat, whereas in man their upper ends have merged, hence the name sternocleidomastoid.

6. The cat has four pectoralis muscles that are partially merged or closely joined with one another. In man they are more closely associated into the pectoralis major and minor.

7. Two rhomboideus muscles, the major and minor, are found in cat and man. In man the major, or posterior, is the larger, whereas in the cat the anterior, or minor, rhomboideus is the larger. The explanation is that the muscles were named first on man, and then the same names were applied to the same muscles in the cat, regardless of the size.

8. The sartorius in man extends obliquely across the inner surface of the thigh from the crest of the ileum to the inner region of the knee, whereas in the cat it extends uniformly along the lateral and anterior surfaces of the thigh.

9. Man has an omohyoid muscle arising on the scapula, extending diagonally across the neck behind the sternohyoid, and inserting on the hyoid bone. The cat has no omohyoid muscle.

10. The gluteus maximum muscle is the largest of the glutei in man but in the cat is smaller than the gluteus medius.

11. The biceps femoris in the cat is relatively large, whereas in man it is relatively small.

12. The serratus posticus superior and inferior are adjacent to one another in the cat, whereas in man they are widely separated.

13. The rectus abdominis in man extends from the fourth rib to the pubic symphysis, whereas in the cat it extends from the third rib to the symphysis.

14. The rectus abdominis is definitely divided by four transverse tendinous intersections in man, whereas in the cat these lines are absent or difficult to identify.

15. The flexor digitorum profundus has five heads, or parts, in the cat, whereas in man it is considered as one muscle, which ends in four tendons on the digits.

16. The median head of the triceps in man is not divided into three parts as it is in the cat.

17. The flexor carpi ulnaris, which appears almost as two muscles in the cat, is not so completely separated in man.

18. The adductor femoris of the cat corresponds to the adductor magnus and the adductor brevis of man.

GENERAL CONCLUSIONS ON MUSCLES

1. It is commonly accepted among anatomists that man's general structure of muscles has become modified, largely because of a gradually acquired, erect position and because throughout man's phylogenetic development muscles have gradually changed to better meet the demands of their activities.

2. A reduction in the number of parts, such as in the muscles of man when compared with those of the cat, is interpreted as an indication of advancement, or higher specialization.

3

General internal organs
of the cat

SURVEY OF INTERNAL ORGANS
(Fig. 47, A to C)

In the study of internal organs, blood vessels, etc., the inexperienced student is often confused concerning which is the right or the left side of the specimen, particularly when it is lying on its back. It is helpful in such cases to think of your own body as lying in the same position as the specimen you are dissecting or which is described. You can always state which is your right or left, dorsal or ventral.

Place the injected cat on its back on the dissecting tray and gradually separate the hind legs. It is best to tie a stout string about three feet long to one of the hind legs and to pass the string under the tray and tie the other end of the string to the other hind leg. Feel the anterior end of the pubic symphysis with your finger. Secure a heavy knife and separate the two pubic bones of this symphysis by cutting between them as indicated in Fig. 47, A. This is often difficult to do. If there is a mounted cat skeleton for you to examine, look at the pubic symphysis carefully before trying to do this. The laboratory assistant can probably give some additional advice to help, since it is important to do this correctly.

After the **pubic symphysis** has been separated, open the body cavity by cutting through the body wall along the **midventral line,** or **raphe,** from the symphysis to

the sternum, being careful not to cut the internal organs. Continue the incision along the left side of the sternum, cutting through the costal cartilages. As you do this, you will see the internal sternal artery and vein along the inner side of the sternum. The **ventral mesentery** will also be seen as a thin membrane extending from the ventral body wall to within the median cleft of the liver, where it is known as the **falciform ligament.** The muscular **diaphragm** consists mostly of skeletal muscle and separates the thoracic and abdominal cavities. Cut the diaphragm on both sides about one inch from the body wall and observe the angle at which it is attached to the body wall. Is its ventral, lateral, or dorsal attachment most anterior? What are the relationships of these attachments to the ribs? Cut on the other side of the entire sternum and remove it.

Both sides of the thoracic wall are to be reflected so that the internal organs may be more easily examined. You may do this by cutting through the first rib with a heavy knife or bone shears; continue to cut through the ribs and body wall, about one-half inch from the spinal column, posteriorward to the diaphragm (Fig. 47, C). The serratus anterior muscle will probably be cut but do not cut the levator scapulae, since it is the only attachment left that holds the left front leg, provided the di-

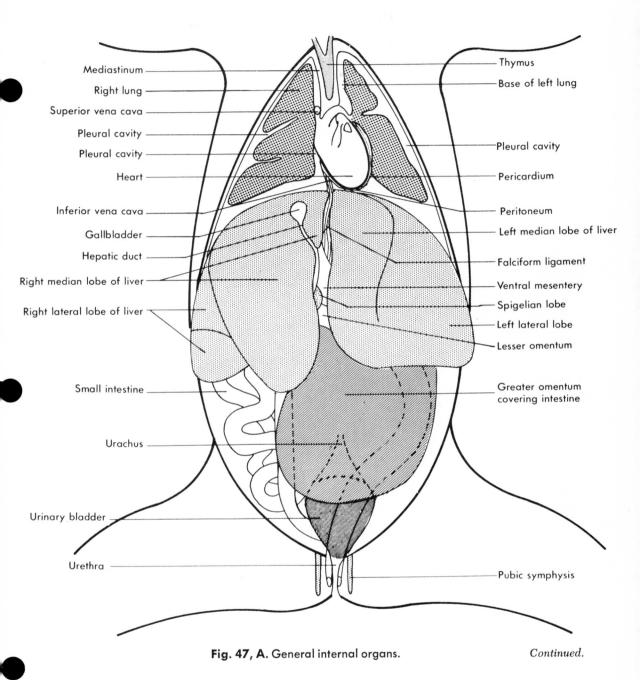

Mediastinum

Right lung

Superior vena cava

Pleural cavity

Pleural cavity

Heart

Inferior vena cava

Gallbladder

Hepatic duct

Right median lobe of liver

Right lateral lobe of liver

Small intestine

Urachus

Urinary bladder

Urethra

Thymus

Base of left lung

Pleural cavity

Pericardium

Peritoneum

Left median lobe of liver

Falciform ligament

Ventral mesentery

Spigelian lobe

Left lateral lobe

Lesser omentum

Greater omentum covering intestine

Pubic symphysis

Fig. 47, A. General internal organs.   *Continued.*

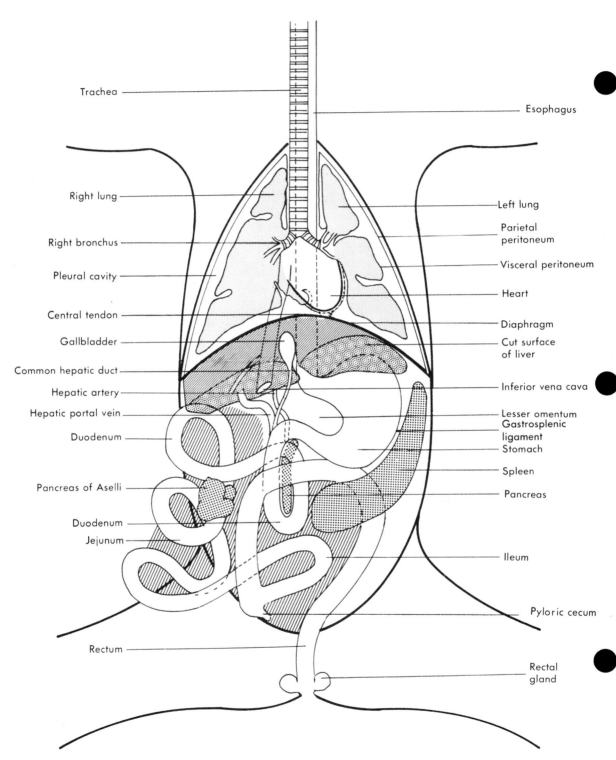

Fig. 47, B. General internal organs; greater omentum, parts of liver, and urinary bladder removed.

Trachea

Right lung

Right bronchus

Pleural cavity

Central tendon

Gallbladder

Common hepatic duct

Hepatic artery

Hepatic portal vein

Duodenum

Pancreas of Aselli

Duodenum

Jejunum

Rectum

Esophagus

Left lung

Parietal peritoneum

Visceral peritoneum

Heart

Diaphragm

Cut surface of liver

Inferior vena cava

Lesser omentum
Gastrosplenic ligament
Stomach

Spleen

Pancreas

Ileum

Pyloric cecum

Rectal gland

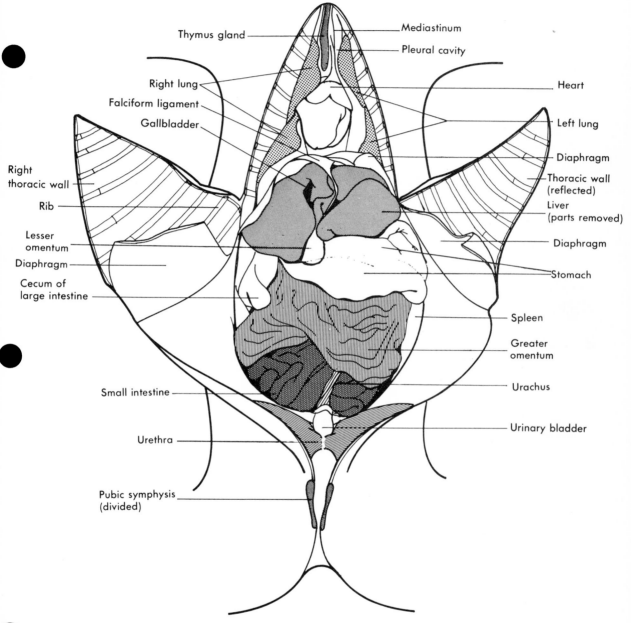

Fig. 47, C. General internal organs, body wall reflected.

Thymus gland

Mediastinum

Pleural cavity

Right lung

Heart

Falciform ligament

Left lung

Gallbladder

Diaphragm

Thoracic wall
(reflected)

Right
thoracic wall

Liver
(parts removed)

Rib

Diaphragm

Lesser
omentum

Stomach

Diaphragm

Spleen

Cecum of
large intestine

Greater
omentum

Small intestine

Urachus

Urethra

Urinary bladder

Pubic symphysis
(divided)

rections for dissection have been followed. The thoracic and abdominal walls are to remain attached to one another on each side below the diaphragm (Fig. 47, C) and are to be put back in place. A string is to be wrapped around the body at the close of each laboratory period.

The fatty mass covering the **intestine** is the **greater omentum.** The thin, shiny parietal peritoneum lines the thoracic and abdominal body walls and both sides of the diaphragm. It is reflected over each of the internal organs, where it is known as serous membrane or visceral peritoneum. Ventral to where the esophagus passes through the diaphragm there is a clear, transparent area known as the **central tendon of the diaphragm** (Fig. 47, A and B). It consists only of the two layers of peritoneum, since the muscular tissue does not enter. Place your fingertip behind the central tendon and examine it closely. This area is the last to close in the embryonic development of the diaphragm, and sometimes this opening persists even in man and is known as a **patent diaphragm.** Adult cats that were apparently otherwise normal have been found with this defect. Sometimes the abdominal organs invade the thoracic cavity through this opening. This condition is called a diaphragmatic hernia. Any marked deviation in structure from the normal is known as an anomaly, and a surgeon should be able to identify one quickly.

Note that the liver is attached at the periphery of its base to the diaphragm by a suspensory ligament, sometimes called the **coronary ligament.** It is the reflection of the peritoneum of the abdominal side of the diaphragm onto the surface of the liver. This attachment is largely a result of its growth in the embryological development of the liver, from the duodenum into the ventral mesentery, a part of which is the septum transversum and which in turn becomes part of the diaphragm.

The **common hepatic duct,** the **gallbladder,** and the **liver** tissue are largely modified parts of the wall of the duodenum and the ventral mesentery from which they develop embryologically.

The various lobes of the liver may differ in size from that shown in Fig. 47, A. Identify the lobes of the liver as follows: **left median,** lying along the falciform ligament and against the left portion of the diaphragm; **left lateral lobe,** between the diaphragm and the cardiac end of the stomach; **right median,** or **cystic, lobe,** lying against the right half of the diaphragm and containing the **gallbladder** within its cleft. The smaller **right lateral lobe** is posterior and lateral to the right median. Its posterior position is partially marked off by a constriction, which extends backward to the right kidney. The **caudate,** or **spigelian lobe** is the smallest of all and is in the median line projecting deeply into the curve of the stomach. The caudate lobe in Fig. 47, A is covered by the ventral mesentery, or **lesser omentum.**

Cut off the lobes of the liver as shown in Fig. 47, B and cut through the median falciform ligament dorsalward to the esophagus. Find the esophagus as it pierces the diaphragm and enters the stomach. Determine the stomach as to position, size, and shape. The end next to the esophagus is called the **cardiac extremity;** the opposite end is the **pyloric.** The **fundus** is the dilated portion of the stomach. The lesser curvature of the stomach indicates the embryonic **ventral,** or **anterior, margin,** whereas the greater curvature indicates the original embryonic **posterior,** or **dorsal margin** where the ventral part of the greater omentum is attached.

Cats with long fur often swallow enough fur when licking themselves to form "fur balls" in the stomach; they may not be passed through the intestine but may cause sickness and are eventually regurgitated through the esophagus and mouth for relief.

The greater omentum is really a part of the two-layered **dorsal mesentery** and extends ventrally from the spinal column. It becomes folded and attached to the posterior edge or greater curvature of the stomach. The **spleen lies** between the two layers of the greater omentum as it extends down as a double-walled bag between the intestines and the ventral body wall (Fig.

47, C). Fig. 47, B shows most of the greater omentum cut and removed. The greater omentum assists in regulating the temperature of the body, and it is also protective because of the many phagocytic cells contained in it. Carefully lift up and unfold the **greater omentum,** beginning at its posterior edge, and you will find that it is a double-walled sac with an opening into it. Insert the little finger of the left hand dorsal to the **ventral mesentery** or lesser omentum at the concave side of the stomach; push your finger posteriorward dorsal to the **pyloric stomach** and into the **cavity** or **bursa** of the greater omentum. This opening is the **foramen of Winslow, or epiploic foramen.** The cavity within the greater omentum is sometimes called the **lesser peritoneal cavity,** or omental bursa, whereas the abdominal cavity posterior to or outside the greater omentum is the **greater peritoneal** or **abdominal cavity.** Between the stomach and spleen is the **gastrosplenic ligament,** which is the two layers of visceral peritoneum.

When the stomach first forms in the embryo, it is in the median position. Then it bends with its concave side ventrally. Following this the stomach turns, bringing its median dorsal line to its extreme left, which is its greatest curvature. It is along this original median dorsal line of the stomach that the greater omentum is attached. The shifting in the position of the stomach in embryological development accounts for the fact that the **right vagus nerve** supplies the dorsal surface of the stomach, whereas the **left vagus** supplies the ventral surface. The **spleen** is a dark, elongated organ lying to the left of the stomach and supported by the greater omentum. It really lies between the two layers of the omentum. It has no ducts, and its products pass directly into the bloodstream. The spleen serves as a reserve blood supply in cases of severe bleeding. Cut off the greater omentum and remove it from the posterior edge of the spleen.

In the bend of the right side of the stomach, as shown in Fig. 47, B, is a thin, ventral mesentery known as the **lesser omen-** tum. The part which continues to the liver constitutes the **gastrohepatic ligament,** and that extending from the liver to the duodenum is the **hepatoudodenal ligament.** Supported by the latter ligament are three important structures. In order to get at these cut away the parts of the lobes of the liver that cover this area and dissect out each of the following structures while holding this ligament on your fingertip (Fig. 47, B). (1) The **common hepatic duct** (ductus choledochus) drains the **liver;** the **cystic duct,** which is short, soon joins it from the **gallbladder,** and the common hepatic duct continues to the **duodenum.** Before entering the **ampulla of Vater,** it is joined by the **Wirsung duct** from the **pancreas.** (2) The **hepatic portal vein** is large and dark because of the coagulated blood or blue because of injecting material. It has thin walls that are easily damaged. (3) The **hepatic artery** is probably injected red. It is small and usually lies between the two previous structures. Place your finger behind this area, tease away the connective tissue of the mesentery, and identify each of these. Cut the right lobe of the liver immediately posterior to the entrance of the **hepatic portal vein** (Fig. 47, B). You may or may not cut the **large postcaval vein.** It passes through the dorsal part of the liver. The cut surface of the liver should show the **hepatic veins,** which are usually empty and are tributaries of the postcava. Blood from the hepatic artery and hepatic portal vein diffuses through the sinusoids of the liver into the tributaries of the hepatic veins, which join the postcava.

The **pancreas** lies along the duodenum and also extends along the posterior edge of the **pyloric stomach** toward the **spleen.** It is often dark brown and varies in size, being smaller in older cats. The pancreas has two ducts: (1) The duct of Wirsung may be found embedded in the pancreas parallel with the duodenum, entering it with the common hepatic duct. (2) The Santorini duct is much smaller and opens into the duodenum two centimeters or more down the duodenum. Its tributaries anastomose with those of the **duct of Wirsung.** If the blood vessels are not well injected within the pancreas, these ducts are difficult to distinguish. To dissect them turn the duodenum to the left side and dissect away the soft parts of the pancreas bit by bit over the fingertip, leaving the connective tissue within which the ducts are embedded. The thymus, pancreas, and sometimes the testes are spoken of as the sweetbread.

Trace the small intestine from the pylorus of the stomach and determine its length. It is very much folded in order to adjust itself to the abdominal cavity. It has no ventral mesentery posterior to the entrance of the common bile duct, but its dorsal mesentery is its principal support; through it pass the arteries, which bring nutriment and oxygen, and the veins, which absorb the nutriment from the digested food from the lumen of the intestine. The **dorsal mesentery** is very much compressed where it joins the dorsal body wall. The lymph capillaries are also in the dorsal mesentery close to the arteries and veins, but they are difficult to see. These absorb fat from the digested food and are called lacteals, since the contents are milklike in appearance. This fat is carried to the thoracic duct (Figs. 52 and 53) and eventually to the left external jugular vein.

Identify the divisions of the small intestines as follows: the **duodenum,** about three and one-half inches long and U-shaped, beside which is the pancreas; the **jejunum,** about eight inches long, which succeeds the duodenum; the remainder is the **ileum,** characterized by its many folds, which joins the large intestine. The transition from duodenum to jejunum is almost impossible to determine accurately from the external surface. When serial microscope slides are examined, they reveal Brunner's glands in the wall of the duodenum and also foliate villi, whereas the jejunum has no Brunner's glands and in the place of leaflike villi has filiform, or long and uniformly slender, villi. The ileum has lymph nodules in its walls, called **Peyer's patches,** near the entrance to the large intestine. The ileum also has short, stubby villi. If microscope slides are available, these various structures may be pointed out

by the laboratory instructor; otherwise their study may be omitted. The principal glands that aid in digestion and the secretions of these glands are as follows: (a) the salivary, which contains ptyalin; (b) the gastric, produces gastric juice, which contains hydrochloric acid; (c) the pancreas, which secretes strongly alkaline juice; and (d) the liver, which produces bile.

There are two kinds of thin, shiny **peritoneum.** (1) The **parietal** peritoneum is the thin, shiny inner layer of the thoracic and abdominal body walls. The kidneys, ureters, and gonads lie behind it, therefore they are called **retroperitoneal.** (2) The **visceral** peritoneum is the thin outer layer of the lungs, thoracic mediastinum, stomach, liver, pancreas, intestines, and spleen and gives rise embryologically to the ventral and dorsal mesenteries, the broad ligament, and the greater omentum.

Spread out the small and large intestine and study the dorsal mesentery. It is really composed of two thin layers that are reflections of the **visceral peritoneum,** which forms the outer serous layer of the intestinal wall. The dorsal mesentery is the main support of the large and small intestines and functions quite well in the cat, whose body is in a **horizontal position,** but in man, whose body is in an **erect position,** it cannot support the intestine efficiently. The result is that the intestine settles down in the abdominal cavity, crowding the **urinary** and **reproductive systems** and complicating their function. This condition, with the accumulation of fat in the greater omentum, causes the abdomen to protrude. The erect position of the body of man makes it a mechanical misfit.

Find the intestinal arteries, injected red, and the veins, blue or dark colored, lying between the two layers. Trace these from the intestine to the large mesenteric lymph gland, or **pancreas of Aselli.** This is a hard mass on the mesentery of the small intestines. Dissect it away and find the dark **superior mesenteric vein.** Refer to Fig. 55, where some of these structures of the digestive system are shown. Turn the intestine over to the right side of the cat and observe the postcava, or **inferior vena** cava, and the injected **dorsal aorta** lying close together near the middorsal line of the coelom. Find the left **adrenal,** or **suprarenal, gland,** a small ovoid mass lying in the fat connective tissue close to the aorta and just anterior to the kidney (see Figs. 48 and 58). It is sometimes difficult to locate. The adrenals and kidneys are retroperitoneal organs, since they lie dorsal to or behind the peritoneum and do not lie in the coelom, or peritoneal cavity.

Find the beginning of the large intestine. The ileum enters it almost at right angles, and the part of the **ascending colon** that projects beyond the union with the ileum is the colic or pyloric cecum. In herbivorous animals such as the **rabbit,** which is about the size of the cat, the cecum is as long and as large as your finger. In the **cow** it is as long and large as your arm. In carnivorous animals such as the cat, the cecum is quite short, and there is **no vermiform appendix.** Several years ago the author of this manual was preparing a lecture on the pyloric cecum and vermiform appendix and was looking up information in the best books available on the subject. In one book on the anatomy of the cat he found the page number in the index for the "appendix" and turned to it; it was the **appendix of the book!** Since then he has remembered **that the cat has no vermiform appendix.** In man the vermiform appendix is atrophied, or vestigial, and varies in length from two to twenty-three centimeters, the average being from eight to nine centimeters. It is longest between ages of ten and twenty years and tends to lose its size and lumen in older years. The evidence from various mammals indicates that the pyloric cecum degenerates to form the vermiform appendix.

Dissect away the small **lymph glands** partially surrounding the **cecum** so that it may be seen clearly. The **ascending colon** is followed by the **transverse colon,** the **descending colon,** and the **rectum.** The large intestine of the cat is supported by a dorsal mesentery, whereas in man the transverse colon adheres tightly against the dorsal body wall. The beginning of the rectum corresponds with that of the first sacral

vertebra, and on each side close to the anal opening is a **rectal,** or **anal, gland.** These are also known as scent glands in many mammals and are especially well developed in the skunk. Refer to Fig. 55.

The **urinary bladder** is an oval-shaped organ posterior and ventral to parts of the intestines (Fig. 47, *A*). Its size varies, depending on the amount of urine it contains. Extending from it to the navel is a suspensory ligament known as the **urachus.** This is a remnant of the embryonic allantoic stalk. The **urethra** drains the urinary bladder to the exterior. The reproductive organs will be considered later.

THORACIC ORGANS (Fig. 47, A and B)

The dorsal and ventral mesenteries are represented in the thoracic cavity by two widely separated layers of splanchnic mesoderm, or visceral peritoneum, called the mediastinum. The **mediastinum** is a septum or partition. It includes the space between the two pleural sacs, or **pleural cavities.** Into this space the **thymus, heart,** and lower ends of the **trachea** and **esophagus** migrate into position in the embryo. From the lower end of the trachea each lung bud pushes laterally and branches, forming a lung, which is covered by the visceral peritoneum of the mediastinum. The lateral wall of the mediastinum also forms the epicardium of the heart, while the pleuropericardial folds give rise to the **pericardium.**

The **thymus** is often darker than the other organs and lies anterior to the heart, within the mediastinum, between the anterior portions of the two lungs. It is elongated and irregular in shape and often bifurcates since it arises from the two sides of the pharynx, or the epithelial lining of the third pharyngeal pouch. The size varies greatly in different cats, being smaller in the older ones. Remove the thymus intact. The mammary arteries and veins supply the thymus and pass along the dorsal side of the sternum, where they are often called the sternal artery and vein; however, they pass through the body wall and supply the anterior region of the mammary glands. The heart is surrounded by a

103

sac, the **pericardium,** and it may be more or less covered with fat. Remove any fat and cut through the pericardium; pull the pericardium from over the heart and cut it off close to its attachments in order to see the heart better. Discard the pericardium. The coronary arteries are usually injected with red latex and are on the walls of the heart.

The **right lung** has four lobes. The **third lobe** is partly divided, and one part extends dorsally to the lower portion of the esophagus into the mediastinum, hence it is often called the **mediastinal lobe.** The fourth and **caudal lobe** on the right side is large and flat. The **left lung** has three lobes. The two **cranial lobes** are partly united at their bases and may be considered parts of a single lobe. Thus the left lung has two distinctly divided lobes. It is known that carbon dioxide is exchanged for oxygen through the walls of the alveoli of the lungs by the process of diffusion.

Observe the **superior vena cava** (Fig. 47, A) entering the right atrium, or auricle, from above and the **inferior vena cava** coming up through the diaphragm, also to the right atrium. The base of the dorsal aorta, or **main aortic arch,** curves to the left, anterior and close to the **heart.** It is probably injected with a colored solution.

Cut off the left lung one-half inch from its base and observe on its cut surface the pulmonary veins, which may be injected red but are usually not injected. The pulmonary arteries are usually injected blue. The bronchial tubes and bronchioli have the most definite walls and may be seen more clearly by mashing the lung slightly and washing away the softer tissue with water. Dry and examine with a hand lens.

There are two pairs of important nerves that pass down through the thoracic cavity. They are not shown in Fig. 47 but are shown in Fig. 71.

1. The **phrenic nerve** may be seen passing ventral to the attachment of the lungs behind the visceral peritoneum or pleura. Look for it on the left side and trace it back through layers of the pericardium until it enters the diaphragm. Now, patiently dissect it forward ventral to the arch of the dorsal aorta and the innominate vein and further forward to its two roots in the neck. Do not confuse it with the fine sympathetic nerve fibers in the region of the aortic arch. They arise in the middle and inferior cervical ganglia and are the accelerator nerves for the heart. The roots of the phrenic nerve arise from the fifth and sixth cervical spinal nerves in the cat but from the third, fourth, and fifth in man. The phrenic nerve is shown on the right side of the cat in Fig. 71.

2. The **vagus,** or **pneumogastric,** is the tenth cranial nerve. It extends from the medulla, through the jugular foramen of the skull, posteriorward close to the common carotid artery, and through the thoracic cavity immediately dorsal to the base of the lungs. Find it here and trace it forward on the left side where it passes ventrally to the arch of the dorsal aorta. Trace it up the neck close to the carotid artery to the **nodosum ganglion** outside the jugular foramen. Dorsal and lateral to the heart the vagus nerve on each side divides into dorsal and ventral branches, which extend about halfway to the diaphragm, where each branch unites with its mate from the opposite side and penetrates the diaphragm to supply the lower esophagus and stomach. As the vagus passes through the thoracic cavity, it is behind or embedded within folds of the peritoneum and is sometimes difficult to dissect satisfactorily.

SOME DIFFERENCES IN INTERNAL ORGANS OF CAT AND MAN

1. Man has a vermiform appendix, whereas the cat has none.

2. The adrenal glands of man are in contact with the kidneys, whereas in the cat they are above or anterior to the kidneys and therefore are sometimes called suprarenal.

3. The left kidney of man is usually higher than the right, whereas in the cat the right is higher or anterior to the left.

4. There are six or more pyramids in the kidney of man, whereas in the cat there are fewer.

5. The pancreas of Aselli is the large lymph gland of the cat located in the mes-

entery of the small intestines. There is no corresponding large lymph gland in man.

6. Much of the thoracic duct of man lies to the right or dorsal to the dorsal aorta, whereas in the cat it tends to lie to the left of the dorsal aorta.

7. The central tendon of the diaphragm of the cat is almost circular, whereas in man it is greatly flattened dorsoventrally, forming right and left leaflets.

8. The liver of man has four lobes, the right, left, quadrate, and caudate or spigelian, whereas the cat has five lobes, the left median, left lateral, right median or cystic, right lateral, and the caudate or spigelian.

9. The pancreas in man consists of a head, neck, and tail and lies along and behind the greater curvature of the stomach. In the cat it is relatively longer and more irregular in shape.

10. The lungs of man consist of a right lung with three lobes and a left lung with two lobes, whereas the cat has a right lung with four lobes and a left with three, not counting the incomplete divisions.

11. The transverse colon of man is closely fused against the dorsal body wall, whereas in the cat there is no such close adhesion.

REVIEW QUESTIONS ON INTERNAL ORGANS WITH THE EXCEPTION OF UROGENITAL ORGANS

1. Of what kind of muscle does the diaphragm consist?

2. Locate the pituitary and thyroid endocrinal glands. (Figs. 6 and 34, *C*)

3. Locate the gallbladder and name the two ducts that help drain it. (Fig. 47, *B*)

4. What is the exact location of the thymus gland in the adult cat? (Fig. 47, *A*)

5. Of what does the greater omentum consist and what are its attachments? (Fig. 47, *C*)

6. What is the urachus? (Fig. 47, *A*)

7. How does it happen that the left vagus nerve supplies the ventral surface of the stomach and the right, the dorsal?

8. Name the organs that constitute the viscera. (Fig. 47, *A*)

9. Locate and describe the falciform ligament. (Fig. 47, *C*)

10. State what is meant by an organ being retroperitoneal; give three examples. (See definition of terms.) (Figs. 48 and 51)

11. Name and locate the two kinds of peritoneum.

12. Name three different structures that are continuous with and are modified parts of the peritoneum. (Fig. 47, A to C)

13. Explain how the greater omentum is a modified part of the dorsal mesentery.

14. What is the relation of the dorsal mesentery to the foramen of Winslow? (Fig. 47, B and C)

15. What is a diaphragmatic hernia and how does it arise?

16. Are the liver, stomach, spleen, and pancreas really within the peritoneal cavity? Why? (Compile the information you have.)

17. Explain the mediastinum of the thorax and name the structures it contains. (Fig. 47, A and B)

18. Explain the structure of the diaphragm and its central tendon.

19. What is the pancreas of Aselli? (Fig. 47, B)

20. Name and locate each of the two bladders of the cat. (Figs. 47, B and 51)

GENERAL UROGENITAL SYSTEM

Fat is usually deposited near the kidneys. Remove this fat and also that in the **groin** surrounding the urinary bladder and covering the ureter. Dissect out the ureter on the left side. It is behind the peritoneum and therefore retroperitoneal. If the greater omentum contains excessive fat, it may be cut off close to its attachment to the stomach and spleen and discarded. Fat is usually deposited around the neck of the **urinary bladder.** Remove this fat by pulling it away with the fingers, being careful not to injure the **hypogastric artery** and **vein** on each side, which extend to the bladder. If you have a male specimen, separate the sperm ducts at the place where one passes forward from each testis along the surface of the muscles lateral to the pubic symphysis and enters the abdominal cavity through the **inguinal canal** (see Fig. 51). Find the ridge of the **symphysis** by pressing with the finger; then cut to separate the two pubic bones, if this has not been done, being careful not to injure the sperm ducts. The urogenital systems of the male and female are constructed on the same general plan. Most of the fully developed structures have corresponding or homologous vestigial organs in the opposite sex. The organs in either sex consist of two principal groups.

1. The **urinary system** consists of the kidneys or metanephroi, ureters, urinary bladder, and the urethra; the pronephros and mesonephros of embryonic development have mostly disappeared.

2. The **reproductive** or **genital system** is composed of the ovaries or the testes with their accessory glands and ducts. The sexes may be distinguished by the external genitalia and by the location of the gonads in the adult. The ovaries are located just posterior to the kidneys, whereas the testes are in the scrotum outside the body. If your specimen is a male, the scrotum may have been removed with the skin, leaving the testes exposed in the anal region. Each student will be required to make a detailed study of the urogenital system of both sexes.

FEMALE UROGENITAL SYSTEM (Fig. 48)

If you happen to have a male specimen, perhaps later you can observe the following structures on some female cat in the laboratory that someone else is dissecting. If your specimen is a male, turn to the discussion of the male urogenital system, which immediately follows that of the female system.

1. The **female urinary system** consists of the following structures. Locate the **kidneys** and the **suprarenal** or **adrenal glands** in the lumbar region. The two names for these glands have come about by the fact that in some animals, as in man, they lie **against** the kidneys, so they are called adrenals; but in some other animals, as in the cat, they are not in contact with the kidneys but lie above or in front, so they are called suprarenals. However, the terms are often used interchangeably.

Pull the fat away from the kidneys, ureters, and bladder with the fingers. Observe that the kidneys are **dorsal** to the peritoneum, hence they are called **retroperitoneal.** The kidneys vary considerably in their relationship to one another, but the right is usually higher in the cat, while the reverse often occurs in man. A single artery goes to each kidney, while usually two veins drain the cat's right kidney. Carefully dissect off the **parietal peritoneum** from the left kidney and its ureter. Occasionally man has two ureters from one kidney, which is an **anomaly.** This is not known to occur in the cat.

Cut the left kidney in half horizontally and observe its cavity, the **pelvis** or **calyx.** The lining of the pelvis is a continuation and enlargement of the wall of the ureter, and it in turn is a diverticulum or outgrowth of the **mesonephric,** or **wolffian, duct** of the embryo. The outer portion of the kidney is the **cortex,** and the **medulla** is under it next to the calyx, consisting largely of radiating **uriniferous tubules** forming pyramids, a portion of which project into the pelvis as **papillae.** In the cat there is usually only one papilla in each kidney, whereas in man there are several in each kidney.

Urine is separated from the blood by the process of **diffusion** in the **glomeruli,** or **malpighian corpuscles.** These are small, oval masses of blood capillaries, epithelial cells, and capsular spaces or renal sinuses, which can be seen only on a microscope

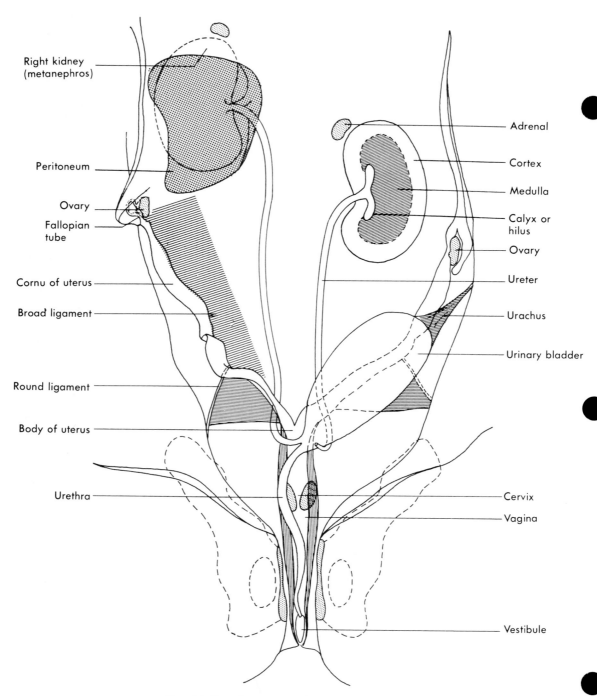

Fig. 48. Female urogenital system, ventral view.

Right kidney (metanephros)

Peritoneum

Ovary

Fallopian tube

Cornu of uterus

Broad ligament

Round ligament

Body of uterus

Urethra

Adrenal

Cortex

Medulla

Calyx or hilus

Ovary

Ureter

Urachus

Urinary bladder

Cervix

Vagina

Vestibule

slide with a compound microscope. The nitrogenous waste of the urine is a by-product of **metabolic activity** of every living cell. It is absorbed and transmitted by the blood to the kidneys, where it diffuses from the blood into the capsular spaces and into the uriniferous tubules mentioned previously. From there it goes into the calyx, ureter, and bladder and is eliminated by the urethra.

The urinary bladder and its supporting ligaments, the urachus, which extends to the inside of the navel, are considered as being extraperitoneal rather than retroperitoneal because they are outside the peritoneum rather than behind it. Observe the place where the ureter enters the bladder and, in the male, the loop of the sperm duct, or ductus deferens, around it. The bladder varies in size, depending on the amount of urine it contains. The urethra of the female drains the urine into the vestibule. Embedded in the urethral walls of the female are two sets of glands, the **paraurethral glands of Skene** and the **vestibular glands of Bartholin.** These are small and cannot be seen with satisfaction in gross dissection. The urethra arises embryologically from the ventral portion of the cloaca, whereas the dorsal part of the cloaca contributes to the extension of the rectum to the anal opening.

2. The **female reproductive system** consists of the following structures. The **ovaries** are slightly larger than a grain of rice and partly covered by the **ovarian ligament,** or **mesovarium,** which supports each. At the anterior end of each cornu of the uterus, next to the ovary, is the **fallopian,** or **uterine, tube,** which is too small to be seen accurately. Eggs from the ovary enter the open end of the fallopian tube. The **cornu of the uterus** extends posteriorly and meets its mate from the opposite side; the two merge together forming the **body of the uterus.** Each cornu is supported by thin mesentery called the **broad ligament.** It consists of a double layer of parietal peritoneum from the body wall. Extending posteriorly and laterally from about the middle of each cornu is the **round ligament.** Its caudal end is attached to the body wall in the approximate position of the inguinal canal of the male. The **cervix** is the constricted area between the body of the uterus and the **vagina,** and it consists of connective tissue fibers and smooth muscle. Dissect these parts out and, if the cat is not pregnant, split them longitudinally. Observe the ovarian artery passing through the **broad ligaments.** Each student in the laboratory should examine the urogenital system of the male also. Perhaps some other student in the laboratory is dissecting a male specimen.

PREGNANT CAT (Figs. 49 and 50)

If your cat happens to be pregnant, you should be able to observe the principal organs involved. The gestation period for a cat is fifty-six to sixty-three days, and comparatively few female cats are obtained for dissection that are in the advanced stages of pregnancy. Midterm should have been reached in order to see the following structures clearly.

1. **Loculi** are enlargements or swellings of the cornu, or horn, of the pregnant uterus, and by counting these the number of embryos, or developing young, may be definitely determined. The cat usually gives birth to four or six young in a litter. The size of each **loculus** is determined by the stage of development, or size of the embryo, and the placenta that it contains. All the young of each litter are about the same size at any one time.

2. Remove one of the anterior loculi by cutting transversely through the uterine wall, both in front and behind it, as well as cutting the broad ligament. Also, remove one side of the loculus by cutting through the outer portion at two opposite sides longitudinally, as shown in Fig. 50. The cut edges of the layers of the loculus or uterine wall can now be identified. (a) The **serosa** is the outer layer, which is thin and continuous with the **broad ligament** and the peritoneal lining of the body cavity. (b) The **muscular layer** which is also thin, is next, but the fibers can be easily seen. (c) The **endometrium,** or **mucosal lining,** is mostly thin but quite thick in the area of the **zonary placenta,** which is the broad band

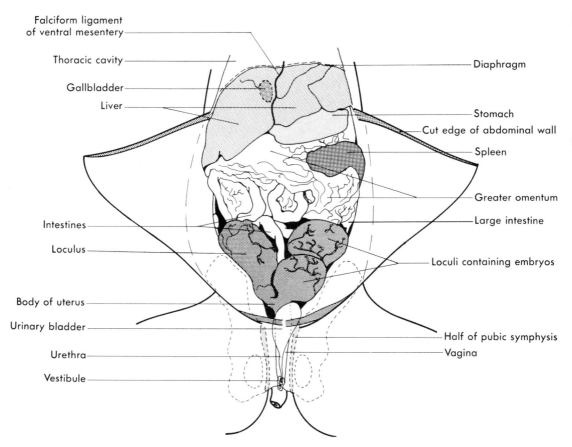

Falciform ligament
of ventral mesentery

Thoracic cavity

Gallbladder

Liver

Intestines

Loculus

Body of uterus

Urinary bladder

Urethra

Vestibule

Diaphragm

Stomach

Cut edge of abdominal wall

Spleen

Greater omentum

Large intestine

Loculi containing embryos

Half of pubic symphysis

Vagina

Fig. 49. Internal organs of pregnant cat.

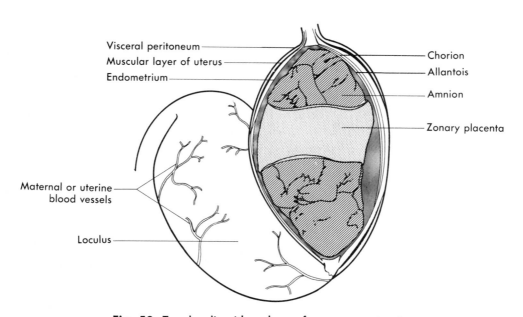

Visceral peritoneum

Muscular layer of uterus

Endometrium

Maternal or uterine
blood vessels

Loculus

Chorion

Allantois

Amnion

Zonary placenta

Fig. 50. Two loculi, with embryos from pregnant cat.

surrounding the center of the embryo. When one side of the loculus was removed, as in Fig. 50, part of the endometrium was divided, part coming off and part left with the embryo. Through these three layers **maternal arteries** bring nutriment and oxygen to the placenta. When the uterine wall was pulled away from the placenta, some of these blood vessels were broken at the places where they entered the placenta against the chorion frondosum part of the chorion.

Observe the **maternal, or uterine, blood vessels** that supply the various loculi. These enlarge during pregnancy, and their capillaries penetrate the walls of the uterus and come to lie in contact with the chorion frondosum to nourish the developing young.

The embryonic, allantoic, or umbilical blood vessels come from the embryo through the umbilical cord and terminate against this same chorion frondosum. Thus the blood vessels of the mother and the embryo come to lie very close to each other but are separated by the **chorion frondosum. Nutriment** and **oxygen** from the maternal, or uterine, arteries diffuse through this membrane into the embryonic, allantoic, or umbilical veins, while waste in the form of carbon dioxide and nitrogenous compounds diffuses from the embryonic, allantoic, or umbilical arteries into the uterine, or maternal, veins.

3. There are really four **embryonic membranes** in all vertebrates above the amphibians, and they will be considered here in order, beginning next to the inner surface of the wall of the cornu, or horn, of the uterus. (a) The **chorion, or serosa,** is the outermost layer of the embryonic membranes. If this layer is slit open near one end of an embryo and the cut edge is examined carefully, you may be able to separate what appears to be one layer into two. The chorion extends into and becomes a part of the placenta. In the placenta it is called the chorion frondosum and is the most significant part of the placenta, because it is through this membrane that all nutriment and waste products must diffuse in reaching or leaving the embryo. The chorion frondosum is thrown, or develops, into projections known as villi. (b) The **allantois** is divided into an outer part, which is here fused with the chorion and which you may have just separated, and an inner layer, which is still closer to the embryo. The wall of the allantois contains the embryonic or umbilical blood vessels, whose capillaries come close to the uterine, or maternal, blood vessels in the villi of the placenta. (c) The **amnion** is the third embryonic membrane and is a very thin layer next to the skin or fur of the embryo kitten. It is very closely fused here with the inner layer of the allantois, so they probably appear as one thin, transparent layer. (d) The **yolk sac** or fourth embryonic membrane develops around the yolk of the microscopic egg and in the mammal dilates as the embryonic membranes develop. The wall of the yolk sac shrinks as its contained nutriment is absorbed, and it is left adjacent to the placenta, whereas its stalk is drawn within the body of the embryo during the first few weeks of gestation. The yolk sac will not be seen outside the body of the developing kitten unless the kitten is less than about one inch long. Parts of the chorion and allantois, with allantoic blood vessels, form most of the embryonic part of the placenta.

4. The fully developed **placenta** is a thickened band or zone surrounding the embryo and because of its shape in the cat is called a "zonary placenta." The placenta is composed of two principal parts. (a) The maternal part consists of a portion of the **mucosal lining,** or **endometrium,** of a loculus. This area is thickened to a rather broad band at places where the villi are located. The uterine, or maternal, blood vessels penetrate the serosa and muscular layers of the loculus of the uterus to reach the placenta proper. (b) The embryonic part consists of a portion of the **chorion** known as the chorion frondosum and a part of the allantois where its umbilical or allantoic blood vessels end against the outer limits of the villi. The walls of the villi constitute the **chorion frondosum.** The amnion does not enter into the placenta but forms a thin, transparent sac or covering for the embryo and becomes continu-

ous with the outer limits of the **umbilical cord.**

Remember that no blood vessels or blood passes from the mother to the embryo or from embryo to mother. Only oxygen, nutritive substances, and a few disease-producing organisms are known to pass to the human embryo, whereas only the carbon dioxide and nitrogenous wastes pass from the embryo to the mother's blood. The embryo has to produce all of its own blood. The embryonic, umbilical, or allantoic blood vessels may be seen on the under or embryonic side of the placenta.

5. The **umbilical cord** is the connection extending from the inner surface of the placenta to the abdominal wall of the embryo, and the umbilical or allantoic arteries and veins may be seen extending through it.

Immediately after the birth of each kitten the placenta loosens, sloughs off from the uterus, and is expelled. The mother cat gnaws the umbilical cord in two, thus freeing the newborn kitten from the afterbirth. Soon after the birth the proximal end of the umbilical cord dries up and sloughs off, leaving the umbilicus, or navel, which is the scar on the outer surface of the abdominal wall of the kitten. Soon after the birth of each of the kittens the afterbirth is expelled and in carnivorous animals is eaten by the mother.

The cat gives birth to from two to eight young in a litter, while the human being normally produces one, occasionally two or three, or very rarely four or even five, as in the case of the **Dionne quintuplets.** These human quintuplets, according to H. H. Newman,[*] "were derived from a single egg. The placenta was single, irregular in outline, not lobed, and had cords of various lengths (probably shorter than seven-month babies), and the five tiny infants weighed only about two pounds apiece at birth." Multiple births in man are interpreted as an **ativistic** characteristic or a so-called "harping back" to an ancestral condition. In the cat the young embryos develop out in the **cornu,** or **horn,** of the uterus, while

in man this normally occurs in the **body of the uterus.** In multiple births the size of each young at birth depends on the amount of blood going to the **loculus** where each develops. The ends of the **cornua** have the least amount of blood. In the case of pigs, in whom from eight to sixteen piglets are produced in a litter, there is often much variation in size of the young at birth. The small ones are called "runts." The gestation period for cats is **fifty-six** to **sixty-three days;** in the pig it is **seventeen weeks,** and in man, it is usually about **thirty-eight weeks** (however in man it is often much less). The cat has a **zonary placenta,** which surrounds the developing young. The **villi,** which are a part of the **chorion,** are, at first, all over the chorion but later disappear, with only a band or zone remaining. During early embryonic life man has the villi all over the chorion, but later the villi disappear, except for a circular area, which at full term is the size of a six-inch pancake and as thick as the palm of your hand. Here we have variation in the distribution of the villi on the placenta of man, which is interpreted as "recapitulation." Recapitulation supports the theory of evolution.

MALE UROGENITAL SYSTEM (Fig. 51)

The **urogenital system** consists of the **urinary** and the **reproductive** systems. The kidneys, ureters, urinary bladder, and urethra form the urinary system. Dissect off the **peritoneum** covering the left kidney and cut it open horizontally. The cavity near the center is the **calyx** or **pelvis,** and the outer portion consists of the **cortex,** which is near the outer surface, and the **medulla,** which is next to the calyx. The **ureter** and the kidney are retroperitoneal. Trace the ureter to the **bladder,** where it is surrounded by a **loop of the sperm duct** before entering. The bladder is supported by a ligament, the **urachus,** which passes from the bladder to the inner position of the **navel.** Most parts of the bladder and the urachus are formed from the embryonic stalk of the allantois.

Separate the **symphysis,** or union of the two **pelvic bones,** if this has not been done

---

[*]Newman, H. H.: Multiple human births, New York, 1940, Doubleday & Company, Inc., p. 104.

114

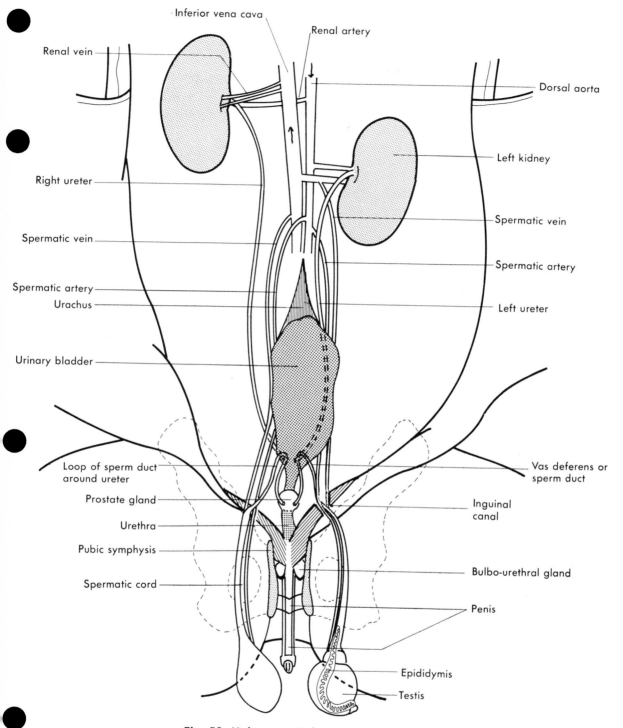

Inferior vena cava

Renal artery

Renal vein

Dorsal aorta

Left kidney

Right ureter

Spermatic vein

Spermatic vein

Spermatic artery

Spermatic artery

Urachus

Left ureter

Urinary bladder

Loop of sperm duct
around ureter

Vas deferens or
sperm duct

Prostate gland

Inguinal
canal

Urethra

Pubic symphysis

Bulbo-urethral gland

Spermatic cord

Penis

Epididymis

Testis

Fig. 51. Male urogenital system, ventral view.

and dissect out the urethra from the bladder to the base of the **penis.** Near the bladder is the **prostate gland** on the urethra, and near the penis is the **bulbourethral gland of Cowper.** Dissect off the skin and scrotum that surrounds the testes. The testes are retroperitoneal during their formation, migration and in the scrotum. Near the testis is a mass of tubules, the **epididymis,** which join the **sperm duct, or ductus deferens,** which in turn passes forward under the skin and enters the body cavity through the **inguinal canal** opening. The wall of the **scrotum** is really an outpouching, or diverticulum, of the abdominal wall and contains the sheaths of the oblique and transverse abdominal muscles.

Trace the sperm duct, or ductus deferens, within the abdominal cavity and find the **loop** around the ureter. This loop occurred because the testis in the embryo was close to the kidney; it migrated down ventral to the ureter and took its blood vessels with it. Near the kidneys the **internal spermatic artery** and **vein** branch from the dorsal aorta and inferior vena cava, respectively, and pass down through the **inguinal canal.** These vessels, together with the **sperm duct** and the **external spermatic nerve,** are enclosed within a sheath called the **spermatic cord,** which extends from the inguinal canal to the testis. Sometimes the abdominal wall weakens in the human male, and the intestines protrude down into the scrotum, producing an **inguinal hernia.** A quite similar condition occurs in the human female, but this is associated with the femoral artery. An operation usually corrects either of these defects.

The embryological development of the kidney of cat or man is quite complicated, since there are what might be called three "kidneys," or **three main parts** for each kidney. These three parts are the (1) **pronephros,** or head kidney; (2) **mesonephros,** or middle kidney; and (3) **metanephros,** or kidney of the adult animal. The first two disappear, for the most part, since in the adult only vestigial remnants, which are not easily seen in gross dissection, remain. See the accompanying chart, page 117.

116

The sperm duct has an unusual history; when it is first formed in the embryo, it is called the **wolffian duct** or **mesonephric duct** and drains the middle kidney, or **mesonephros.** When the permanent kidney, or **metanephros,** forms in the older embryo, the mesonephros almost completely disappears.

Some of its uriniferous tubules remain and connect with the **testis** and become the **efferent ductules of the epididymis** in the male or the **epoophoron** in the female. Other uriniferous tubules become vestigial. The mesonephric, or **wolffian,** duct becomes the **sperm duct, or ductus deferens,** for the passage of sperm. In the female the **wolffian duct** becomes the vestigial **Gartner's duct.** Since the urethra is a duct for both urine and sperm in the male, it functions as a urogenital duct, but it is only urinary in the female. The **epididymis** consists of the convoluted portion of the efferent ductules, or mesonephric tubules, and of the **sperm duct** by the side of and against the testis.

3. **Homologies.** The urogenital organs of the male and female in cat or man are built on the same general plan. In the young embryo the sex organs are undifferentiated and hence are given **generalized terms,** as in the middle column of the accompanying chart. Organs having the same origin and general structure are said to be **homologous.** Here we often see the same generalized structure of the early embryo becoming different organs in the adult male and female.

Sometimes the male or female reproductive organs do not differentiate completely into a typical anatomical male or female but become partly developed reproductive organs of both male and female in one individual. This occurs in many groups of animals, including the human being. Such individuals are called **hermaphrodites** or **intergrades.** Man's body does not always follow a certain strict standard anatomical pattern.

It is interesting to know that in the embryological development of the cat or man there is a **brief summary** or **review** of the structure or kinds of the kidneys of various groups of lower animals. This is revealed by the kidneys of *myxinoid Cyclostomis* and a **few bony fishes,** in which the **pronephros** is the functional kidney in the adult and the mesonephros and metanephros do not form. The **lamprey, most fishes,** and the **amphibians** have the **pronephros** in their early development but only the functional **mesonephros** as adults. **Reptiles, birds,** and **mammals** have the **pronephros** in early embryonic development, the **mesonephros** in later embryonic development, but only the functional **metanephros** as adults.

Thus, when the kidneys pass through stages in their development that are similar to those of the adults of lower vertebrates, as the preceding facts show, it is known as **recapitulation.** These facts are interpreted by most embryologists and anatomists as supporting the theory of **evolution.**

SOME DIFFERENCES IN UROGENITAL SYSTEMS OF CAT AND MAN

1. The female cat has a bipartite uterus, whereas the female human has a simplex uterus.

2. The right kidney of the cat is located more forward or anterior than the left kidney, whereas in man the left kidney is higher in the body than the right.

3. Usually two renal veins drain the right kidney of the cat. This condition is found less often in man.

4. Usually six or more medullary papillae, or pyramids, are found in each of man's kidneys, whereas the cat usually has only one.

5. The fallopian tubes are relatively much longer in the female human than they are in the cat.

6. Cat embryos develop in the horns, or cornua, of the uterus, whereas in man the embryos develop in the body of the uterus.

7. The ovaries of the cat are located relatively higher in the abdominal cavity than they are in man.

8. The ductus deferens of man enters the urethra immediately below the bladder, where the prostate gland is located, whereas in the cat the ductus deferens enters the urethra some distance below the bladder; its prostate gland is also at this place.

9. The seminal vesicles are well developed in man but are poorly developed or absent in the cat.

10. The placenta of man is discoid, whereas in the cat it is zonary.

11. The cornua of the female cat's reproductive system usually develops several loculi, in each of which a single embryo and its placenta develop. In the female human one embryo and its placenta usually develop in the body of the uterus.

12. In the male cat an inguinal hernia seldom if ever occurs, whereas in man it is not unusual. Its common occurrence in man is partly because of the erect position of the body.

Comparable urogenital organs

Adult male	Young embryo	Adult female
Disappears	Pronebhros	Disappears
Efferent ductules	Mesonephros	Epoophoron
Kidney	Metanephros	Kidney
Ureter	Diverticulum of wolffian duct	Ureter
Urinary bladder	Parts of cloaca and allantoic stalk	Urinary bladder
Urachus	Part of allantoic stalk	Urachus
Urethra	Ventral part of cloaca	Urethra
Testes	Gonads	Ovaries
Sperm duct, or ductus deferens	Wolffian duct	Gartner's duct (is degenerated)
Vagina masculinus, or prostatic utricle (is degenerated)	Müllerian duct	Fallopian tube, uterus, and vagina
Prostate gland	Urethral glands	Paraurethral gland, or gland of Skene
Bulbourethral, or Cowper's gland	Urethral glands	Vestibular glands, or gland of Bartholin
Penis	Phallus	Clitoris
Scrotum	Muscles and skin	Labium majora

REVIEW QUESTIONS ON UROGENITAL SYSTEMS

1. What parts of the urogenital system are retroperitoneal? (Figs. 48 and 51)

2. What duct conducts germ cells from the testis? the ovary? (Figs. 48 and 51)

3. How long is the gestation period of the cat?

4. How does the size of the cornu of the uterus adjust itself to the developing embryos? (Figs. 48 to 50)

5. What are the names of the four principal embryonic membranes? (Fig. 50)

6. Which two embryonic membranes become most involved in the formation of the placenta? (Fig. 50)

7. Describe how nutriment within the maternal, or uterine, artery finds its way into the bloodstream of the embryo.

8. How does the nitrogenous waste within the circulation of the embryo reach the blood vessels of the mother cat? (Fig. 48)

9. What happens to the embryonic membranes when the young are born?

10. Explain the term mediastinum. (Fig. 47, C, and definitions of terms)

11. Name the structures that are homologous in the adult male and female urogenital systems. (Figs. 48 and 51)

12. Give in the corresponding order the name of the duct, or tube, that drains the following structures: (1) ovary, (2) urinary bladder, (3) testis, (4) kidney, and (5) gallbladder.

13. Trace the passage of sperm cells, or spermatozoa, from the testis until eliminated from the body. (Fig. 51)

14. Name two endocrinal glands of the abdominal cavity. (Figs. 47, B, and 48)

15. Name the duct that takes urine to the bladder and the duct that takes urine away from the bladder. (Fig. 51)

16. Why is the gland above the kidneys in mammalian animals sometimes called **adrenal** and other times called **suprarenal?**

17. What is an inguinal hernia?

18. Name the glands on the urethra of the male and the comparable glands of the female. (Fig. 51)

19. What is the gestation period of the cat? of man?

20. Are the testes of the cat or man within the body cavity or are they retro-peritoneal? (Fig. 51)

4

Venous and lymphatic systems of the cat

INTRODUCTION

The blood system is a two-way system in that the arteries carry oxygenated blood laden with nutriment from the heart out over the body, where oxygen and nutriment diffuse through the walls of capillaries to supply the various cells, which in turn give off carbon dioxide and broken-down substances of metabolism. This waste material diffuses into the venous capillaries, which unite to form veins that return this blood to the heart. The superior and inferior venae cavae are the two principal vessels entering the heart. The larger arteries and veins tend to run parallel with one another, but many variations exist as a result of their early formation in the embryo as a fine meshwork, or network, of capillaries. The blood begins to flow along a certain course, which is not always the same in a given area in different animals. These vessels that carry most of the blood enlarge, while others remain relatively small. Therefore blood vessels, particularly veins, in cats differ not so much in the area supplied or drained as in the way they connect with larger vessels. In **dissecting** or **surgery** one needs to know not only the places where blood vessels usually are located but also, if not there, the places where they are then most likely to be found in relation to adjacent muscles and nerves. Veins usually vary more in their positions and branchings than do arteries. As you dissect, compare your specimen with others in the laboratory and note these anomalies.

The **lymphatic system** is a one-way system in that lymph flows only toward the heart, or, to be more exact, toward the large veins that take the lymph with the blood to the heart. The **thoracic duct** or main trunk of the lymphatic system is shown as two parallel broken lines in Figs. 52 and 53 of the venous system. It comes up the body to the left of the precaval and postcaval veins.

TRIBUTARIES OF SUPERIOR VENA CAVA (PRECAVA OR DESCENDING VENA CAVA) (Fig. 52)

There is considerable variation in the veins of the cat. There is variation in the way they unite with one another and also in the way they are injected. Therefore the veins on your cat may not be exactly as in the following description. Dissect off the thymus gland, previously identified, the fat anterior to the heart, and the pericardium, which is the membranous sac surrounding the heart. The **superior vena cava** is the largest, dark-colored vessel entering the heart on its cephalic surface. Its principal tributaries are as follows.

1. The **azygos vein** is the tributary of the precava close to the heart. Cut off the lobes of the right lung of the cat close to its base.

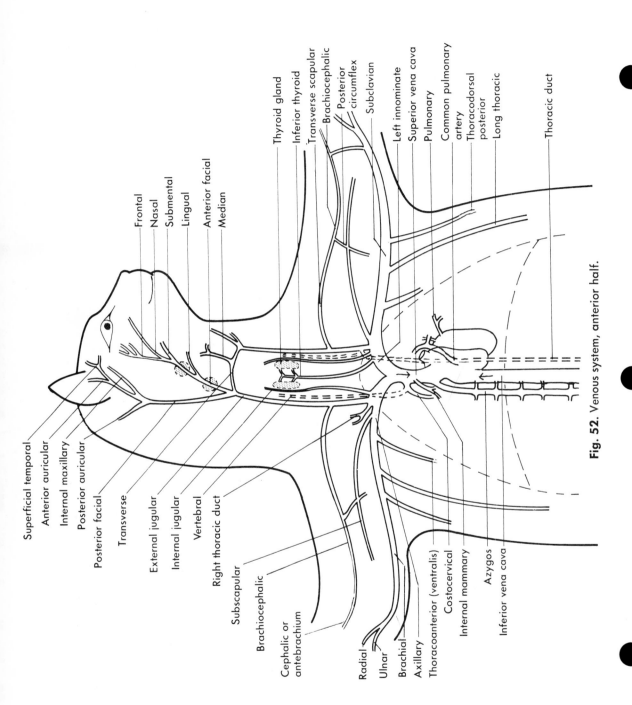

Superficial temporal
Anterior auricular
Internal maxillary
Posterior auricular
Transverse
External jugular
Internal jugular
Vertebral
Right thoracic duct

Subscapular

Brachiocephalic

Cephalic or
antebrachium

Radial
Ulnar
Brachial
Axillary
Thoracoanterior (ventralis)
Costocervical
Internal mammary
Azygos
Inferior vena cava

Frontal
Nasal
Submental
Lingual
Anterior facial
Median

Thyroid gland
Inferior thyroid
Transverse scapular
Brachiocephalic
Posterior
circumflex
Subclavian

Left innominate
Superior vena cava
Pulmonary
Common pulmonary
artery
Thoracodorsal
posterior
Long thoracic

Thoracic duct

Fig. 52. Venous system, anterior half.

122

Pull the heart over to the cat's left side and observe the azygos vein on the right side close against the spinal column. It is large and arises close to the diaphragm. The tributaries of the azygos are the **intercostals** from the body wall. The **azygos vein** is only on the right side, and the word "azygos" means unpaired.

2. The **sternal** or **mammary vein,** previously identified, is the second tributary into the superior vena cava. It passes through the thin portion of the mediastinum close to the thymus gland and along the inner surface of the sternum. It then passes through the thoracic body wall and in the female is known as the mammary, because it supplies the mammary glands. The two innominate veins unite to form the superior vena cava.

3. The **costocervical vein** may join the superior vena cava or the right innominate. It extends posteriorly across the bases of the first few ribs. Sometimes the costocervical on the right side is joined by the vertebral. When this occurs, its base is called the **costocervical axis** (see description under tributaries of the innominate vein).

4. The **vertebral vein** may join the innominate vein independently. If so, lift up the right innominate and find the vertebral vein entering the transverse foramen of the last cervical vertebra. The vertebral vein is shown by broken lines in Fig. 52. It conducts blood from the neck and head. The left vertebral joins the left innominate, or subclavian. The **innominate** on each side is formed by the union of the external jugular and the subclavian veins. Dissect out the base of the **right external jugular.** This is the large, dark vessel close to the skin as it comes from the head and passes deeper to join the subclavian. Its tributaries will be dissected later.

5. The **axillary vein** is the name given the subclavian immediately outside the thoracic wall. The **axilla** is the armpit. The first tributary of the axillary on the right side is a small, short, difficult-to-find **right thoracic duct.** This is interpreted as being the remnant of a much larger thoracic duct of more primitive ancestors. The tho-

racic duct on the left side will be dissected later.

6. The **brachial vein** is the part of the subclavian through the upper arm, distal to the axillary vein. It has three principal tributaries. The **subscapular vein** comes from the dorsal muscles of the upper arm, and it may be joined by the posterior circumflex from the brachiocephalic, or cephalic humeral, vein, previously seen when dissecting the deltoid muscles. Three principal tributary veins come from the pectoral region, or the thoracic wall. (a) The most median is the **thoracoanterior,** or **ventralis,** from the pectoralis muscles. (b) The next laterally is the **long thoracic,** which extends caudally along the inner portion of the serratus anterior and pectoralis muscles. In the female it drains the area of the anterior milk glands, where it is called the external mammary. (c) The **thoracodorsalis** is more lateral and drains the lower portion of the latissimus dorsi and pectoralis muscles.

TRIBUTARIES OF INNOMINATE VEIN (Fig. 52)

1. The right **costocervical vein** often enters the **innominate vein;** however, it may have a common base with the **vertebral** in the region of the first rib. Therefore it is mentioned in both groups. In this case they form the costocervical axis, which enters the **superior vena cava** close to the **internal mammary vein.** Dissect the right vertebral to the place where it emerges from the transverse foramen of the seventh cervical vertebra. The **left vertebral vein** is quite different, as shown in the drawing (Fig. 52).

2. The **internal jugular vein** arises at the base of the skull and extends down the neck beside the trachea close to the **common carotid artery** and the **vagus nerve.** It usually enters the innominate vein but may enter more anteriorly into the external jugular vein.

3. The **subclavian vein** comes from the brachial region of the front leg and receives the **subscapular vein,** the base of which may be almost parallel to the external jugular vein.

4. The **external jugular vein** from the head and neck lies just under the platysma muscle on the ventrolateral surface of the neck. It joins the subclavian on each side to form the **innominate vein.**

5. The **thyroid vein** drains the upper part of the trachea; between the **thyroid glands** it passes down the ventral surface of the trachea and enters the left innominate vein.

TRIBUTARIES OF SUBCLAVIAN VEIN (Fig. 52)

The **subclavian vein** is more specifically the proximal part of the main vein from the foreleg under the clavicle. It unites with the **external jugular vein** to form the **innominate,** and in the axilla, or the place where the forelimb joins the body, the subclavian is called the **axillary vein.** More distally in the upper arm, or brachium, it is known as the **brachial vein,** which is formed by the union of the **radial** and **ulnar veins** (from the forearm) with the radial on the thumb side. Dissect out these veins and their tributaries on the left leg as follows, beginning close to the entrance of the left external jugular vein.

1. The **subscapular vein** comes from the underside of the scapula and usually enters the axillary portion of the subclavian close to the base of the external jugular (see Figs. 29 and 52). The subscapular usually has a connection with the **brachiocephalic vein** or the **transverse scapular vein,** which is under the scapula close to the shoulder joint. This connection is the **posterior circumflex vein,** previously mentioned when discussing the shoulder muscles. The transverse scapular is a continuation of the brachiocephalic after it ceases to be superficial. The former joins the external jugular and its tributaries will be considered in the next group of veins.

2. The **thoracoanterior,** or **thoracoventralis,** vein is small and joins the axillary vein close to the first rib. It extends ventrally and drains the pectoral muscles close to the sternum. This vein and the two following are quite variable concerning the place where each joins the axillary vein. Seldom can each of the three be traced their full extent in the same cat.

3. The **long thoracic vein** arises along the inner surface of the pectoralis minor muscle near the outer edge of the mammary gland, runs forward along the median side of the latissimus dorsi, and joins the axillary portion the subclavian or sometimes the subscapular. After the long thoracic vein leaves the mammary region it is called the external mammary. The tributaries of the subclavian vein vary in different specimens, and the descriptions here will not be accurate for all cats.

4. The **thoracodorsal vein** arises from the upper chest wall under the scapula and joins the axillary portion of the subclavian usually close to the **posterior circumflex vein,** which is on the level with the lateral surface of the body wall.

5. The brachial portion of the subclavian receives the **radial** and **ulnar veins** near the inner side of the bend at the elbow.

6. The **cephalic antibrachium vein** is on the lateral surface of the forearm and is continuous with the brachiocephalic or, by means of a **median cuboid vein,** joins the brachial vein near the elbow. Dissect each of these veins so that all may be demonstrated. Remember that the instructor can usually tell at a glance whether or not a serious attempt has been made to dissect them. Color each of the foregoing veins on Fig. 52.

TRIBUTARIES OF EXTERNAL JUGULAR VEIN (Fig. 52)

Dissect away the fascia and muscles covering the right external jugular vein and identify the following veins.

1. The **transverse scapular vein** flows into the lower portion of the external jugular. It comes from the shoulder anterior to the scapula, where it receives blood from the **brachiocephalic,** previously mentioned.

2. The main **thoracic,** or **lymphatic duct** of the **lymphatic system** enters the base of the **left external jugular vein** after passing up the thoracic region close to the **inferior vena cava,** behind the peritoneum and dorsal to the left innominate, to enter the **left external jugular** close to the **innominate** or **subclavian.**

3. The **right lymphatic duct,** which was previously mentioned, is short and incon-

spicuous. Look for it behind the **peritoneum** close to the base of the **right external jugular,** or it may enter the **subclavian.** It is usually difficult to identify, but sometimes it is beaded and relatively large. It is believed to be a **remnant** of a right thoracic duct, a mate to the left.

4. The **transverse jugular vein** extends across from the opposite side near the hyoid cartilage and may have one or more median vein tributaries.

5. The **anterior facial vein** arises between the eye and the mouth by the union of the **frontal** and **nasal veins.** It receives the **submental vein** near the angle of the mouth. The anterior facial vein passes posteriorward close to the lymph glands and receives the **lingual vein.** It usually joins with the transverse jugular vein before merging with the posterior facial.

6. The **posterior facial vein** is formed by tributaries from the side of the head and region of the ear. The **posterior auricular vein** usually joins the **superficial temporal vein** below the parotid salivary gland to form the posterior facial vein, which passes lateral to the submaxillary gland to join the **anterior facial vein.** The superficial temporal is formed by tributaries at the back of the eye and usually receives the **anterior auricular vein** and a deep subfacial or **internal maxillary vein.** Sometimes the two auricular veins have a common base before joining the superficial temporal.

COMPARISONS OF THE SUPERIOR VENA CAVA AND ITS BRANCHES IN CAT AND MAN

The external jugular vein in the cat is larger than the internal jugular; hence it is interpreted that the subclavian and external jugular veins units to form the innominate vein. However, in man the internal jugular is larger than the external jugular vein, and therefore it is interpreted that the subclavian and internal jugular veins unite to form the innominate vein.

TRIBUTARIES OF INFERIOR VENA CAVA, OR POSTCAVA (Fig. 53)

1. Dissect out the inferior vena cava from the right atrium to the diaphragm and find the **phrenic veins** embedded in the posterior or anterior walls of the latter.

2. The **hepatic veins** are embedded deep in the liver and will be considered later in connection with the hepatic portal system.

3. The **adrenolumbar veins** differ on the two sides in the way they drain the **suprarenal,** or **adrenal, glands** and body wall. What relationships do these veins have to the kidneys? These and the following veins may be observed as they pass toward the inferior vena cava.

4. The **renal veins** return blood from the kidneys. This blood has had most of its nitrogenous waste removed as it passed through the glomeruli of the kidneys (Fig. 51). This waste will find its way as urine into the ureters and the urinary bladder to be eliminated through the urethra. Two renal veins are sometimes found on the right side and, more rarely, two on the left.

5. The **right spermatic vein** of the male (Figs. 51 and 53) or the **right ovarian vein** of the female enters directly into the inferior vena cava, but on the left side more often each enters the left renal vein. Examine the specimen closely and note these differences. The spermatic veins are often not well injected, since they are small and the injecting material must pass the valves in the wrong way.

6. The **superior** and **inferior mesenteric veins** bring blood from the **small intestines** and **large intestines,** respectively, to join in the formation of the **hepatic portal vein,** which divides into the **small portal veins** in the liver. These are not direct tributaries of the **inferior vena cava** but are shown superimposed on the kidneys and inferior vena cava in Fig. 53. They will be considered in detail in a subsequent exercise.

7. The **iliolumbar veins** drain the small of the back and are closely associated with the arteries of the same name.

8. The **common iliacs** are the two tributaries that unite in the pelvic region to form the inferior vena cava. The **right common iliac** receives the **caudal,** or **sacral, vein** from the tail. Sometimes there is also one on the left. Each common iliac is formed by (a) the **external iliac,** or **femoral vein,** which is the large principal vein from the leg, and (b) the **internal iliac,** or

125

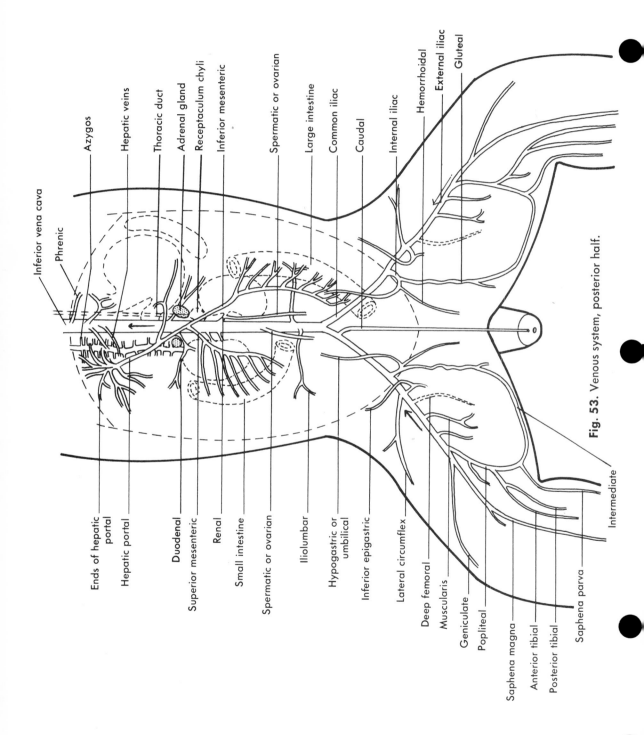

Inferior vena cava

Phrenic

Azygos

Hepatic veins

Thoracic duct

Adrenal gland

Receptaculum chyli

Inferior mesenteric

Spermatic or ovarian

Large intestine

Common iliac

Caudal

Internal iliac

Hemorrhoidal

External iliac

Gluteal

Ends of hepatic portal

Hepatic portal

Duodenal

Superior mesenteric

Renal

Small intestine

Spermatic or ovarian

Iliolumbar

Hypogastric or umbilical

Inferior epigastric

Lateral circumflex

Deep femoral

Muscularis

Geniculate

Popliteal

Saphena magna

Anterior tibial

Posterior tibial

Saphena parva

Intermediate

Fig. 53. Venous system, posterior half.

126

hypogastric, vein, which unites with the external iliac near the body wall. Sometimes the two common iliacs extend forward separately to the region of the kidneys, where they unite to form the inferior vena cava. When this occurs, it is considered an anomaly, or a marked deviation from the normal structure.

TRIBUTARIES OF EXTERNAL AND INTERNAL ILIAC VEINS (Fig. 53)

The **right** and **left common iliac veins** extend from the lower end of the postcava, or inferior vena cava, to the abdominal wall, where each is formed by the union of the long **external** and the short **internal iliac veins.**

1. Tributaries of the **external iliac,** or **femoral, vein** are as follows. The right leg of the cat is to be dissected from the ventral or median surface, but there are so many variations that the following descriptions may not be accurate in all details for any one cat. Veins are named according to the structures they drain—not in the way they unite with one another.

(a) The **circumflex femoral lateralis vein** branches from the external iliac near the body wall and extends laterally and dorsally to the proximal end of the sartorius muscle. Dissect out the base of this vein and bisect the sartorius muscle to expose its extremity.

(b) The **inferior epigastric vein** comes from the groin on the inside of the ventral body wall and, in the female, from the lower mammary glands.

(c) The **deep femoral,** or **profundus, vein** has its base immediately beyond the inferior epigastric. It comes over the anterior surface of the adductor femoris muscle and accompanies the deep femoral artery. Sometimes this vein is not injected. The broken lines indicate its deep position (Fig. 53).

(d) Two or more **muscularis veins** arise at about the center of the dorsal surface of the gracilis muscle and join the external iliac, which is now called the femoral, at about the center of the thigh. The femoral vein is parallel and usually median or posterior to the femoral artery.

(e) The **superior articular,** or **geniculate, vein** comes from the region of the kneecap and is close to the surface. It extends up the thigh to join the femoral vein.

(f) The **saphena magna** is superficial, or next to the skin, coming up along the inner side of the calf of the leg and extending across the lower part of the gracilis muscle, accompanied by the saphena artery and nerve to its union with the popliteal and superior articular, or geniculate, vein to form the femoral, or external iliac, vein.

(g) The **popliteal vein** comes from the deep, lower, posterior region of the thigh across the popliteal space, mentioned with the dissection of the semitendinosus and semimembranosus muscles. Remove the adipose tissue (posterior to the knee) in the popliteal space with the fingers instead of with the scalpel, so as not to injure the popliteal vein and artery. Within the fat is also located the small **popliteal lymph gland.** There are several tributary veins to the popliteal. Unless they contain blood or are injected, they may not be identified.

(h) The **inferior saphena parva vein** comes up the superficial posterior surface of the calf of the leg and joins the **intermediate vein,** which brings blood down from the posterior region of the thigh to form the popliteal vein (Figs. 44 and 53). However, the blood may flow up the intermediate vein and enter the **gluteal vein,** which is a tributary of the internal iliac. The gluteal will be mentioned in more detail later. Other tributaries of the popliteal are the **anterior** and **posterior tibial veins.** Their bases may be seen as they join the popliteal and then may be traced down into the calf of the leg. Quite often these veins are poorly injected.

2. Tributaries of the **internal iliac vein** (hypogastric vein in man) are few in number. The internal iliac as such is very short. Expose its base near the body wall by reflecting the gracilis, semimembranosus, and adductor femoris muscles and observe that its three tributaries unite close together.

(a) The **hypogastric vein,** sometimes called the umbilical, comes from the lateral wall of the urinary bladder and passes caudally and dorsally to join with the other

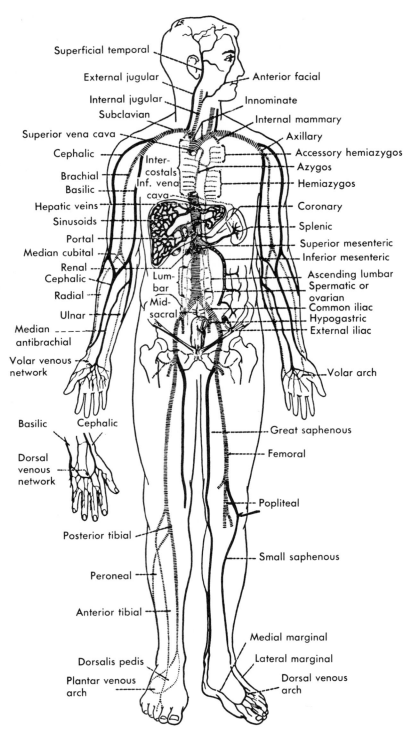

Fig. 54. Human venous system. The deep veins are cross hatched; the superficial veins are solid. (From Millard, N. D., King, B. G., and Showers, M. J.: Human anatomy and physiology, Philadelphia, 1956, W. B. Saunders Co.)

two tributaries. This vein brings oxygenated blood from the placenta to the embryo before birth through the umbilical cord, hence the name **umbilical vein.**

(b) The **hemorrhoidal vein** arises close to the pubic symphysis and rectum and passes forward to the internal iliac.

(c) The **gluteal vein** is difficult to trace even when well injected. Dissect it from the ventral surface and trace it through the deep upper part of the thigh to the dorsal surface, where it is usually easily seen. On the better specimens it may be traced down the thigh until it joins the **saphena parva vein** by an **intermediate vein** to form the popliteal. In some specimens the gluteal may join the common iliac vein.

HEPATIC PORTAL SYSTEM
(Figs. 53 and 55)

The tributaries of the hepatic portal vein drain the walls of the digestive tract and its mesenteries below the **diaphragm.** It also drains the pancreas, spleen, and the greater and lesser omenta. The hepatic portal system consists entirely of veins that begin as capillaries associated with the aforenamed organs and ends in sinusoids in the liver. There is much variation in the veins that drain the **stomach, pancreas,** and **spleen,** and those shown in Fig. 55 may not be accurate for your particular specimen. Remember that veins are named from the organs they drain and not by the manner in which they unite with one an-

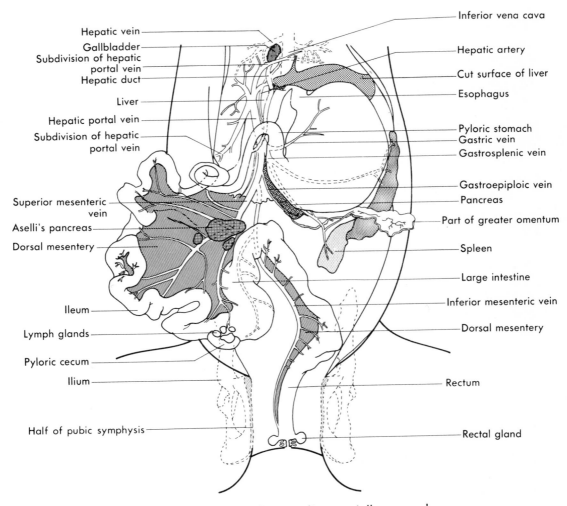

Fig. 55. Hepatic portal system, liver partially removed.

129

other. This system is often not injected, and thus its smaller vessels are more difficult to identify. In Fig. 55 the posterior portions of the liver lobes and most of the greater omentum are shown as having been removed. Following are the more important veins that unite to form the hepatic portal vein.

1. The **superior mesenteric vein** arises in many small tributaries in the wall of the **small intestine** and **ascending colon.** Most of these vessels extend through the thin dorsal mesentery and unite with one another near an enlarged lymph gland, the **pancreas of Aselli.** This gland is an irregular mass about the size of the end of the thumb. Dissect it away and find the superior mesenteric vein.

2. The **inferior mesenteric vein** arises in the wall of the descending colon, extends forward through its mesentery, and joins the sueprior mesenteric vein. There is much variation in the manner in which the tributaries unite to form the portal vein, hence Fig. 55 may not accurately represent these veins on your cat.

3. The **pancreaticoduodenal vein** is small and drains part of the **duodenum** and a portion of the **pancreas adjacent** to it. It can usually be seen on the proximal bend of the duodenum as it extends forward to enter the portal vein. The pancreaticoduodenal is often difficult to identify because it is wholly or partially surrounded by adjacent tissue. Examine the dorsal surface of the lesser omentum, where it is sometimes exposed with little or no dissection as dark or blue in color.

4. The **gastroepiploic vein** drains the posterior wall of the pyloric portion of the stomach, pancreas, and usually portions of the spleen and **greater omentum.** It passes forward dorsal to the pyloric opening of the stomach to join the portal vein, or sometimes it joins the pancreaticoduodenal vein. It is small and often difficult to trace. The **greater omentum,** as shown in Fig. 55, has been mostly removed.

5. The **coronary vein** is small and drains the region of the lesser curvature of the stomach close to the cardiac opening. It extends through the **lesser omentum** to join the gastrosplenic, or sometimes it connects directly with the portal vein.

6. The tributaries of the **gastrosplenic vein** drain most of the spleen and dorsal wall of the stomach as they pass across its dorsal side to unite into one vein before joining with the common mesenteric to form the large **common hepatic portal vein.**

The tributary veins of the **hepatic portal vein** absorb carbohydrates and proteins, largely from the walls of the small intestines. These are transported to the liver by the large **hepatic portal vein,** where it branches and rebranches, ending in interlobular veins and portal sinusoids between the radiating cells of the liver lobules. From here the blood enters the intralobular or central lobular veins, which are tributaries of the **hepatic veins,** and hence into the **inferior vena cava.** The sinusoids are in contact with the liver cells, which absorb the excess carbohydrates in the blood and stores them in the form of glycogen. Later this glycogen is "doled out" as needed into the **intralobular** or **central veins,** which connect with hepatic veins, the inferior vena cava, and all over the body. The hepatic portal system and the liver regulate the amount of carbohydrates in the blood. A prepared microscope slide and a compound microscope are necessary to see these smaller vessels.

COMPARISONS OF THE VENOUS SYSTEMS IN CAT AND MAN (Figs. 52 to 56)

1. Compare the diagrams of the inferior vena cava and its tributaries in cat and man (Figs. 53 and 54).

2. Perhaps the most striking difference is that caused by the **great saphena** (saphena magna), which is relatively larger and longer in man, passing up the thigh and joining the external iliac in the pelvic region; in the cat the saphena magna joins the femoral a short distance above the knee.

3. The internal iliac and its branches are relatively less conspicuous in man; however, the hypogastric is present in both.

4. The caudal vein is relatively large in the cat in comparison with its homologue in

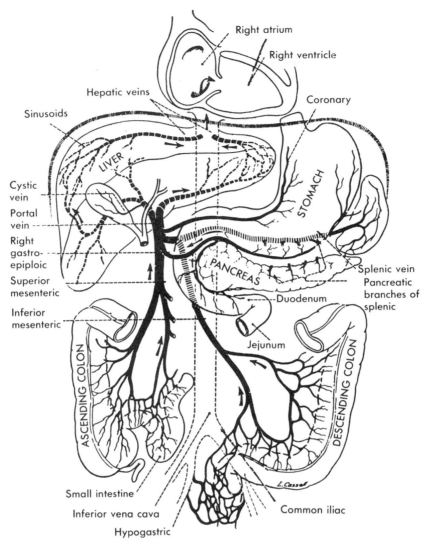

Right atrium

Right ventricle

Hepatic veins

Sinusoids

Coronary

LIVER

STOMACH

Cystic vein

Portal vein

Right gastro-epiploic

Superior mesenteric

PANCREAS

Splenic vein

Pancreatic branches of splenic

Inferior mesenteric

Duodenum

Jejunum

ASCENDING COLON

DESCENDING COLON

Small intestine

Inferior vena cava

Hypogastric

Common iliac

L. Cassel

Fig. 56. Portal system of the veins of man. The transverse colon and small intestine have been partially removed, and the organs have been separated in order to show the vessels. (From Millard, N. D., King, B. G., and Showers, M. J.: Human anatomy and physiology, Philadelphia, 1956, W. B. Saunders Co.)

man, the middle sacral vein (see Fig. 59).

5. In man there is no intermediate vein connecting the popliteal vein with the lower end of the gluteal inferior vein as in the cat.

6. In the erect position of man the blood in the veins of the leg and most of the body has to flow upward against gravity. Often there is not enough push, and it starts down the leg against the valves, producing the knotty enlarged condition known as **varicose veins.** There is no known record of cats having varicose veins.

REVIEW QUESTIONS ON REPRODUCTIVE AND VENOUS SYSTEMS

1. Why do the principal spermatic arteries and veins which supply the testes, arise near the kidneys rather than in the pelvic region? (Figs. 53, 54, and 58)

2. What are the main contents of the spermatic cord as it passes through and beyond the inguinal canal? (Fig. 51)

3. Name two embryonic tissues and one maternal tissue that give rise to the placenta. (Fig. 50)

4. What three layers make up the wall of the uterus? (Fig. 50)

5. Why is it that the urethra is strictly a urogenital duct in the male but is not in the female? (Figs. 48 and 51)

6. Name and locate three different kinds of glands that aid in digestion. (Fig. 47, *B*)

7. What is an hermaphrodite?

8. Which organs resemble the lymph glands and are called lymphoid organs?

9. What are phagocytes and where are they produced?

10. Name and locate five endocrinal glands.

11. Trace the blood from the popliteal vein to the left lung. (Figs. 52 and 53)

12. What anomalies have you observed in the study of veins? (Rely on your own observation and make a small sketch to show.)

13. What are the principal parts of the hepatic portal system? (Fig. 55)

14. What is the cornu of the uterus? (Fig. 48)

15. What is the broad ligament and where is it located? (Fig. 48)

16. What are the three kinds or parts of the kidneys embryologically?

17. What two glands are on the urethra of the female?

18. Why does the sperm duct loop around the ureter in the male? (Fig. 51)

19. Do embryos of the cat develop in the body, or cornu, of the uterus? Where do embryos develop in the human being? (Figs. 48 to 50)

20. Name the four embryonic membranes of the pregnant cat. (Fig. 50)

21. What constitutes the afterbirth?

LYMPHATIC SYSTEM (Figs. 52 and 53)

The lymphatic system is a one-way system, since its lymph flows only toward the heart. Its capillaries are all over the body, adjacent to the skin, internal organs, brain, and bones, but are so small that they are seldom seen in ordinary dissection. It receives lymph from three minute sources: (1) from **arterial capillaries, or sinusoids,** of lymph glands, spleen, thymus, and tonsils where it receives various white blood corpuscles and the plasma; (2) from the **small lymph sinuses** close to the various cells of the body, where it receives toxic or poisonous, broken-down by-products of the metabolic or physiological processes of the cytoplasm; and (3) from the **lymph capillaries** in the walls of the small intestine known as **lacteals,** which absorb the fats of digestion, called **chyle.** Fats filter through the pancreas of Aselli, previously mentioned, which is the largest gland in the cat. Its size is related to the flesh- or fat-eating, or carnivorous, animals. The lymphatic system filters its lymph through the lymph glands and returns these inactive substances to the venous system, which in turn takes them to the heart and hence to the lungs and kidneys where most unusable or injurious substances are removed from the blood and eventually eliminated from the body. It must be remembered that the lymph glands are most effective because of the activities of their phagocytic cells, which render many toxic substances harmless before they enter the bloodstream.

The red blood cells in the adult originate in the marrow of the long bones and pass directly into the veins.

The following structures are the principal parts of the lymphatic system.

The **thoracic duct** is shown in Figs. 52 and 53. It is thin walled, usually reddish brown in color, and about the size of the lead in a pencil. It is often "beaded" or irregular in size because of the dilations caused when the lymph flows backward against the numerous valves. The duct is often seen behind or dorsal to the peritoneum of the thoracic cavity, close against the dorsal aorta immediately above the diaphragm. With a dissecting needle carefully dissect off the peritoneum that covers it. The thoracic duct mostly lies ventral to the intercostal arteries but passes dorsal to them in the upper thoracic region. Dissect the thoracic duct posterior to the diaphragm where it dilates into the **receptaculum chyli,** or **cisterna chyli.** Posterior to the kidneys, small lymphatic tributaries may be seen uniting to form the duct. Trace the thoracic duct forward as it passes behind the **left innominate vein** and left subclavian artery. It soon makes a bend to the left and enters the left external jugular vein in the cat, while in man it opens into the **left subclavian vein.** The lymph in the lymphatic system is believed to flow continuously, largely by the steady absorption of lymph from arterial and venous capillaries and sinuses, by movements of muscles, and probably by some pressure from the heartbeat through arteries and sinuses. If the venous system is well injected, some of the injecting fluid may have gotten past the valves and into the upper part of the thoracic duct.

There are many hundreds of lymph glands (nodes or nodules). Most of them are quite small and are embedded mostly in the fascia and connective tissue, so they are not usually seen.

In man many fairly **large lymph glands** are located in the groin, axilla of the arm, at the base of the lungs, about the heart, in the upper neck region, and about the mammary glands. **Cancer cells** are often found within these glands or nodes, and infection spreads from one to another; hence in many operations it is necessary to remove these centers of infection.

In the cat the **main lymphatic duct** from the **pancreas of Aselli** to the **receptaculum chyli** often has a beaded appearance caused by lymph backing up against the valves. Small, uninjected lymph vessels are sometimes seen in the mesentery of the small intestines. Here they are called **lacteals,** since they **absorb** and **transport** chyle, which contains fat. As chyle or lymph filters through the glands, lymphocytes and monocytes, two of the most important leukocytes, are added to the lymph and thus find their way into the blood system.

The **second main trunk** is the **right lymphatic duct,** which drains the right side of the thorax, right forelimb, and the right side of the neck and head. Identify it as it enters the **right external jugular vein,** near the place where this vein enters the subclavian. The **tonsils, thymus,** and **spleen** are known as **lymphoid organs,** since they resemble lymph glands histologically and are considered modified lymph glands. The lymphatic system is sometimes called a **salvaging system,** since it helps conserve many substances that can be reused by purifying and returning them to the blood circulation.

SOME DIFFERENCES IN VEINS AND LYMPHATIC VESSELS OF CAT AND MAN (Figs. 53 and 54)

1. The external jugular vein is larger than the internal jugular vein in the cat, whereas the internal jugular vein is larger in man.

2. Two veins usually drain the right kidney of the cat. This condition occurs less often in man.

3. The thoracic duct enters the left external jugular vein in the cat but enters the left subclavian vein in man.

4. The thoracic duct in the cat has a relatively larger portion that is bifurcated or double than in man.

5. In the cat the brachiocephalic vein connects with the transverse scapular, whereas in man this vein enters directly into the subclavian vein.

6. Several lymph glands are relatively larger in the cat than in man.

7. The two innominate veins in the cat are approximately the same length, whereas in man the right innominate vein is about half as long as the left.

8. The thoracic duct of man lies on the right side of the center below the diaphragm, whereas in the cat it is on the median line in this region.

9. The great saphenous vein of the thigh and lower leg is a major superficial vessel in man but is relatively much smaller in the cat.

10. In man a posterior external jugular vein drains the back of the head and neck and enters the external jugular vein on the lateral surface of the neck. The cat does not have the posterior external jugular vein.

11. In man there is a hemiazygos vein on the left side of the chest that is absent in the cat.

REVIEW QUESTIONS ON LYMPHATIC SYSTEM

1. What are the names of the principal parts of the lymphatic system? (Figs. 34, *B*, 52, 53, and 55)

2. Where does the thoracic duct join the venous system in the cat and in man? (Fig. 52)

3. Explain how the lymphatic system is a one-way system, whereas the blood system is a two-way system.

4. Where are the principal lymph glands, or nodes, located?

5. Why are lymph vessels occasionally beaded?

6. Name and locate each of the lymphoid organs. (Fig. 47, *C*)

7. What blood corpuscles are known to originate in lymph nodes or glands?

8. What peculiar cells enable the lymph glands to function most effectively?

9. What is the general distribution and location of lymph capillaries?

10. What is the difference between visceral and parietal epithelium? (Fig. 47, *B*)

11. If the lymph vessels constitute a one-way system of circulation, how is lymph able to flow more or less continuously? Where does the lymph come from?

12. Explain what happens to bring about an inguinal hernia.

13. Describe how nutriment and oxygen within the maternal, or uterine, artery find their way into the embryo.

14. What are the main contributions of the spleen and lymph glands to the blood?

15. What organs are sometimes called the sweetbread?

16. What is the difference between a patent diaphragm and a diaphragmatic hernia?

17. Locate and explain the foramen of Winslow.

18. What is the principal function of the spleen?

19. Does the cat have a vermiform appendix? Explain. (Fig. 47, *B*)

20. What is the mediastinum of the thorax, and what does it contain? (Fig. 47, *A*)

5

Arterial system and heart of the cat

In specimens properly prepared for dissection the arteries have been injected with red latex or a colored starch mass. A careful dissection of these vessels will probably reveal that all do not branch or lie in exactly the same position as given in the following descriptions. In a former exercise, when the thoracic organs were identified, the fat and pericardium surrounding the heart were dissected off. Identify the **aortic arch,** which is the bend of the base of the **dorsal aorta,** to the left of the entrance of the **superior,** or **precaval, vein** with the **azygos.** Note that the aortic arch curves to the left and passes posteriorly along the middorsal line of the abdominal cavity. This aortic arch represents the fourth, or systemic, arch, which has persisted on the left side of the embryo. Find the branches given off in the following order.

ARTERIES WITH BASES WITHIN THORACIC CAVITY (Fig. 57)

1. The **coronary arteries** are usually injected with red latex and are found in the ventral and dorsal walls of the heart. They arise from the deep base of the **aortic arch,** which cannot be seen well until the heart is dissected later (see Fig. 61). The coronary veins open into the coronary sinus, which opens into the right atrium. These parts usually are poorly injected because the injection is made against the valves.

2. The **pulmonary artery** extends from the right ventricle (Fig. 60) as a common duct between the two atria on the ventral side of the heart. This vessel divides ventral to the aortic arch, and an **artery** carries impure blood to each lung. These are probably injected blue and should be colored blue in the drawing. In order to expose the arteries better, cut the superior vena cava below the base of the sternal, or mammary, veins and pull the innominate veins forward. As this is done, observe the vertebral veins passing dorsalward to enter the transverse foramina of the last cervical vertebra; they also pass through each of the transverse foramina of the cervical vertebrae up to the skull.

3. The **vertebral artery,** indicated by the dotted line in Fig. 57, is by the side of the vertebral vein, on the right side of the cat, as it enters the transverse foramen of the last cervical vertebra. Do not dissect further. It is small and will probably be seen for only about a centimeter. The two vertebral arteries extend forward and unite along the ventral surface of the brain to form the **basilar artery.** Its dotted lines indicate its deep position (see Figs. 57 and 70).

4. The **innominate artery** is the first and largest branch from the aortic arch. It frequently gives off the **left common carotid artery** first and then divides into the **right subclavian** and the **right common carotid arteries.** There is considerable variation in

139

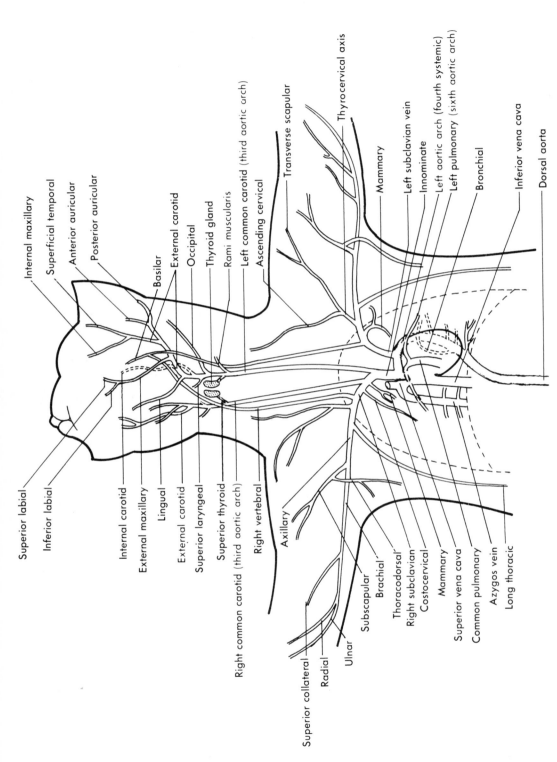

Fig. 57. Arterial system, anterior half.

140

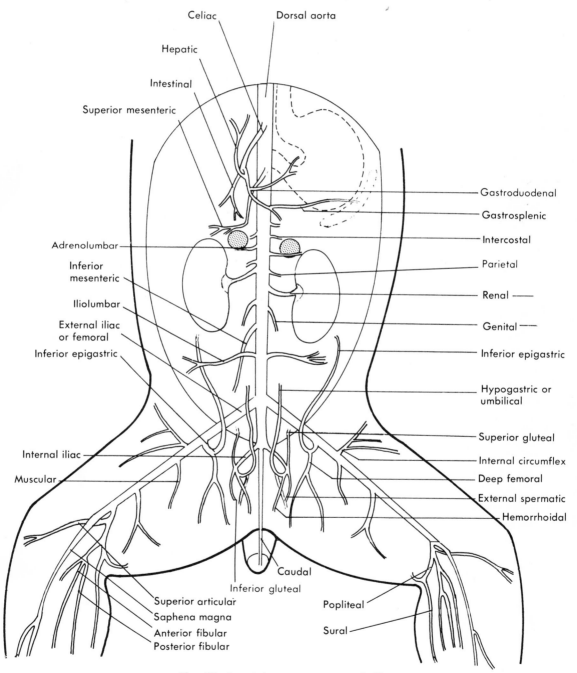

Fig. 58. Arterial system, posterior half.

Celiac

Dorsal aorta

Hepatic

Intestinal

Superior mesenteric

Gastroduodenal

Gastrosplenic

Intercostal

Adrenolumbar

Parietal

Inferior
mesenteric

Renal ———

Iliolumbar

Genital ——

External iliac
or femoral

Inferior epigastric

Inferior epigastric

Hypogastric or
umbilical

Superior gluteal

Internal iliac

Internal circumflex

Muscular

Deep femoral

External spermatic

Hemorrhoidal

Caudal

Inferior gluteal

Superior articular

Saphena magna

Popliteal

Anterior fibular

Sural

Posterior fibular

the manner in which the innominate divides, but in the majority of cases it is similar to that shown in Fig. 57. Examine other cats in the laboratory for differences.

5. The **right subclavian artery** branches from the innominate, but the **left** branches directly from the **aortic arch** of the dorsal aorta, close to the heart. The artery is designated by different names as it extends into the arm, as is the subclavian vein, previously discussed. In the armpit it is called the "**axillary artery,**" in the upper arm, the "**brachial artery.**" Occasionally the right subclavian arises from the aortic arch between the bases of the innominate and the left subclavian arteries and passes dorsal to the innominate artery, the trachea, and the esophagus. This condition is considered an anomaly. If possible, examine other cats in the laboratory to observe variations in the branches of the subclavian, innominate, and carotid arteries.

6. The **internal mammary arteries** arise from each subclavian artery close to the first rib, and they extend posteriorly and ventrally on each side of the mediastinum to the sternum, ventral to the heart. Often they can be traced through the ventral thoracic wall in the pregnant cat and lateral to the rectus abdominis muscles, where they extend caudally and are known as the superior epigastric arteries. These anastomose with the inferior epigastric arteries, which branch from the external iliac, or femoral, arteries. The inferior epigastric arteries are large in the pregnant or lactating female; they come through the abdominal wall just anterior to the pubic symphysis, then they turn forward and supply the posterior mammary glands (Fig. 58).

7. The **intercostal arteries** may be seen on the right side, branching from the subclavian close to the base of the mammary, but they can be seen best on the left side posterior to the aortic arch of the **dorsal aorta,** where they supply the muscles close to the ribs.

8. The **bronchial arteries** branch from the dorsal aorta, dorsal and slightly posterior to the heart, and extend forward to the base of the lungs. Pull the heart over to the right side to find them entering the base of the left lung. If they are not well injected, probably you will have difficulty identifying them. These arteries, with the **bronchial veins,** constitute the **nutritional circulation** to the lungs. The circulation through the **pulmonary arteries** and **veins** constitutes the **functional circulation** of the lungs.

9. The **phrenic artery** arises from the dorsal aorta close to the diaphragm and should be seen on its anterior or posterior side.

Color it red to indicate purity and add arrows to show direction of flow.

ARTERIES TO UPPER PART OF NECK AND HEAD (Fig. 57)

The branches of the common carotid artery lie median to the salivary glands; hence they should be considered again before being mutilated. Therefore, turn to Fig. 34, where the salivary glands and adjacent veins are shown. After these are identified return to this page. Dissect the following arteries so that they can be demonstrated to the instructor or anyone else.

1. Start with the **left common carotid artery** at the place where it branches to form the **innominate artery.** Dissect away the muscles and connective tissue and expose it and its branches up into the head. There is much variation in these blood vessels, hence it is almost impossible to describe them accurately. They are named as determined by the part or parts supplied and not by the position where they branch off from the larger trunk.

(a) The **rami muscularis artery** is small, extends dorsally, and supplies the levator scapula ventralis muscle of the neck.

(b) The **superior thyroid artery** is small and extends medially near the thyroid cartilage to the **thyroid gland** and the sternothyroid and sternohyoid muscles.

(c) The **superior laryngeal artery** branches off about a quarter of an inch anterior to the superior thyroid artery and extends medially to muscles of the larynx.

(d) The **occipital artery** has its base almost opposite the base of the superior laryngeal artery. It is long and extends forward to the deep muscles of the neck and the occipital region of the skull.

2. The **common carotid artery** divides at the base of the skull into the **external carotid artery** and the deep **internal carotid artery,** which is indicated by dotted lines in Fig. 57. It may be difficult to find. We shall now consider each of these two divisions.

(a) The **external carotid artery** has several branches, mostly on the side of the head, as follows:

(1) The **lingual artery** is fairly large as it branches from the external carotid near the bend and enters near the center of the extreme posterior portion of the tongue (see Fig. 34, *C*). The lingual usually extends some distance nearly parallel with the hypoglossal nerve, which also extends forward to enter the tongue.

(2) The **external maxillary artery** branches from the external carotid and passes beneath the digastric muscle toward the corner of the mouth, where it divides into several branches, the most important being the **superior** and **inferior labials,** to the upper and lower jaws, respectively.

(3) The **posterior auricular artery** branches from the external carotid and goes posterior to the auditory meatus, whereas the **anterior auditory artery** passes anterior to the meatus. These two arteries usually have a common base.

(4) The **superficial temporal artery** branches off between the ear and the corner of the mouth to supply the region between the base of the ear and the eye.

(5) The **internal maxillary artery** is considered as a continuation of the external carotid forward from the base of the superficial temporal to supply the maxillary region.

(b) Dissect out the base of the **internal carotid artery** slightly posterior to the origin of the **lingual artery** and expose it among the deep muscles, as indicated by the dotted line in Fig. 57. In Fig. 70 the internal carotid is shown entering the circle of Willis from each side. The arteries supplying the ventral surface of the brain will be considered after the brain has been removed from the skull and a discussion of its structure has been given. Color and add arrows to indicate the direction of flow in Fig. 57.

ARTERIES TO LOWER PART OF NECK AND ANTERIOR LIMBS (Fig. 57)

Return to the **right subclavian artery** as it leaves the innominate. Within the thoracic cavity the name subclavian is used; just outside the thoracic wall the name **axillary** is applied; in the upper arm the name **brachial** is often used; however, the name subclavian is sometimes used incorrectly to include the last two names also. Examine the right subclavian at the place where it gives off the following arteries but remember that the relative positions of the bases of the first four differ in various cats. Identify the vagus and phrenic nerves as they pass ventral to the subclavian artery as it leaves the thoracic cavity. According to the author's arrangement the first three arteries are included in two groups and therefore are presented again.

1. The **vertebral artery** branches from the subclavian before it leaves the thoracic cavity. It was discussed previously.

2. The **costocervical artery** arises from the ventral surface of the subclavian artery in the region of the first rib close to the base of the vertebral artery, turns back, crossing the bases of several ribs, and gives off the transverse colli. These branches pass through the body wall and supply the levator scapula and serratus anterior muscles.

3. The **mammary artery** extends ventralward, usually from a point close to the base of the costocervical, and turns caudally, passing through the body wall to the mammary glands. In the region below the diaphragm this artery is known as the **superior epigastric artery.** In the lactating cat this artery is enlarged and extends further posteriorward, anastomosing with the inferior epigastric, which is a branch of the external iliac artery. These two pairs of epigastric arteries supply all the mammary glands.

4. The **thyrocervical axis** arises close to the base of the mammary but extends forward and branches immediately into the **ascending cervical** to the deep muscles of the neck and the **transverse scapula,** which passes over the shoulder accompanied by the transverse scapular vein.

5. The **long thoracic artery** branches from the axillary and extends to the middle

of the pectoralis muscles and onto the latissimus dorsi.

6. The **subscapular artery** branches from the axial or proximal end of the brachial, lateral to the base of the long thoracic, and soon gives off the **thoracodorsal,** which passes laterally and caudally, usually between the subscapular and teres major muscles. The thoracodorsal supplies the latissimus dorsi, teres major, and epitrochlear muscles (see Fig. 29).

7. The **brachial artery** gives off the **superior collateral** and the **profundus** but divides before reaching the elbow into the **radial artery,** which passes through the **supracondyloid foramen** and the **ulna** and supplies the flexor digitorum profundus muscle. The median nerve accompanies the radial artery through the supracondyloid foramen.

ARTERIES OF ABDOMEN AND POSTERIOR LIMBS (Fig. 58)

1. The **celiac artery** arises from the dorsal aorta immediately posterior to the diaphragm and soon divides into three main branches: (a) the **hepatic artery,** which gives off the gastroduodenal to supply the pyloric portion of the stomach, and the pancreaticoduodenal artery, which supplies the pancreas and duodenum; the main hepatic artery passes to the liver parallel with the common hepatic duct and the portal vein; (b) the **left gastric artery,** which supplies the lesser curvature of the stomach and part of the ventral surface, which is its embryonic left side; (c) the **gastrosplenic artery,** which is the largest of the three and which supplies the dorsal side of the spleen and a portion of the greater omentum.

2. The **superior mesenteric artery** arises close behind the base of the celiac artery, passes between the celiac and anterior mesenteric ganglia and divides into the pancreaticoduodenal artery, which supplies the pancreas and duodenum. The large middle colic artery supplies the transverse descending colon, and the ileocolic artery supplies the lower part of the ileum, the cecum, and the descending colon.

3. The **parietal arteries** are many and supply the body wall on each side of the dorsal aorta; if they are large, they may also supply other organs, as do the adrenolumbars and iliolumbars, which will be considered later. The small parietals may be seen in the upper abdominal region coming directly from the dorsal aorta.

4. The **adrenolumbar artery** arises from the aorta posterior to the superior mesenteric. One branch extends forward to the suprarenal gland, where the main trunk continues into the body wall. The **phrenic artery** sometimes branches from the adrenolumbar or even the femoral and supplies the diaphragm, but these conditions are considered anomalies. It is often poorly developed or not injected.

5. A **renal artery** supplies each kidney, but the two do not arise at the same level. Sometimes they branch before entering the kidney.

6. The **genital** (**internal spermatic** or **ovarian**) **arteries** in the male or female, respectively, are slender and arise posterior to the renal artery. If you have the male, trace the spermatic artery to where it leaves the body through the inguinal canal and down to the testis. The ovarian artery is much shorter and supplies the ovary. Embryologically, the testis differentiates close to the kidney, where its blood supply is established; then the testis migrates through the inguinal canal, taking the blood vessels and nerves with it. Usually the ovary migrates comparatively little.

7. The single **inferior mesenteric artery** passes to the lower colon and the rectum.

8. The **iliolumbar arteries** supply the small of the back and lie quite parallel with the iliolumbar veins.

The dorsal aorta extends into the pelvic region and gives off on each side two large arteries, the external iliac, or femoral, into the hind leg and the internal iliac, which supplies most of the pelvic region. The dorsal aorta continues as the small **caudal,** or **sacral, artery** into the tail. Sometimes this artery branches from the right internal iliac. Dissect the bases of these vessels, going down deeply in the pelvic region to find the base of the caudal artery.

9. The **external iliac,** or **femoral, artery**

has many branches, and for convenience the discussion is here divided into various parts. Dissect the right leg and find the following branches.

(a) The **deep femoral,** or **profundus, artery** branches off medially near the body wall and breaks up into the **inferior epigastric artery,** which extends forward on the inner side of the abdominal wall close to the rectus abdominus muscle. It is enlarged and continues forward on the pregnant or lactating cat and connects with the superior epigastric. The superior and inferior epigastric arteries supply the mammary glands. The second branch of the short deep femoral in the male is the **external spermatic artery,** which supplies the external genitalia.

(b) The **lateral circumflex artery** extends laterally, not far from the base of the profundus, and passes under the median posterior edge of the sartorius muscle. The external iliac continues down the thigh and is known as the **femoral artery** (see Fig. 42).

(c) Two or more **muscularis arteries** branch medially and turn in between the adductor femoris and semimembranosus muscles.

(d) The **saphena magna artery** is a large artery that is a branch from the femoral artery and lies immediately under the skin. It passes superficially over the lower end of the gracilis muscle, continues diagonally across the median side of the shank, and is accompanied by the saphena magna vein. Below the knee it divides into the **dorsal** and **ventral saphenous arteries.**

(e) The **superior articular,** or **geniculate, artery** passes toward the patella. It is closely associated with and sometimes passes through the vastus internus muscle to the median side of the patella. Accessory blood vessels in this region are common.

(f) The **popliteal artery** is one of the main divisions of the femoral. It passes through the popliteal space at the back of the knee. It is accompanied by the popliteal vein and usually passes between the plantaris and inner head of the gastrocnemius muscles (see Fig. 46, *A*).

(g) The **anterior tibial** and **posterior tib-**ial arteries extend in the region of the tibia, and the **sural artery** extends into the lower posterior part of the shank and foot.

10. The **internal iliac artery,** as previously stated, arises from the dorsal aorta immediately posterior to the base of the external iliac. Several branches are soon given off, but usually none of these is well injected.

(a) The **umbilical artery,** or **hypogastric,** of man, sometimes called the **internal iliac,** is the largest branch and supplies the urinary bladder. It is the remnant of the allantoic, or umbilical, artery of embryonic circulation to the placenta. Sometimes these names are applied to the internal iliac.

(b) The **superior gluteal artery** extends median to the ischium and supplies the bases of the tensor fasciae latae, sartorius, and rectus femoris muscles.

(c) The **hemorrhoidal artery** goes to the lateral wall of the rectum and urethra. In the female it extends forward to the uterus and its cornu.

(d) The **inferior gluteal artery** arises near the base of the hemorrhoidal, passes under the pyriformis muscle, and divides into branches to the pyriformis, glutei, and caudofemoris muscles. Its base is parallel with that of the sciatic nerve.

Add arrows to indicate the direction of blood flow.

Compare Figs. 57 and 58 with Fig. 59. Note the differences and the similarities.

RELATIONSHIPS OF HEART (Fig. 60)

It is necessary to remove the heart from the body in order to dissect it properly. To do this the pericardium must be removed, and the lungs must be cut off close to their bases. Identify each of the following structures and cut it off according to directions.

1. The **superior vena cava** is formed by the union of the two **innominate veins.** Cut the innominates off at about the center of their course. Lift up the precava and identify the costocervical and **mammary veins.** Cut each of these off close to its base. The **azygos vein,** which enters the superior vena cava close to the heart, is to be cut also.

2. Cut the **inferior vena cava** above the diaphragm.

3. Cut the **right subclavian artery** half-

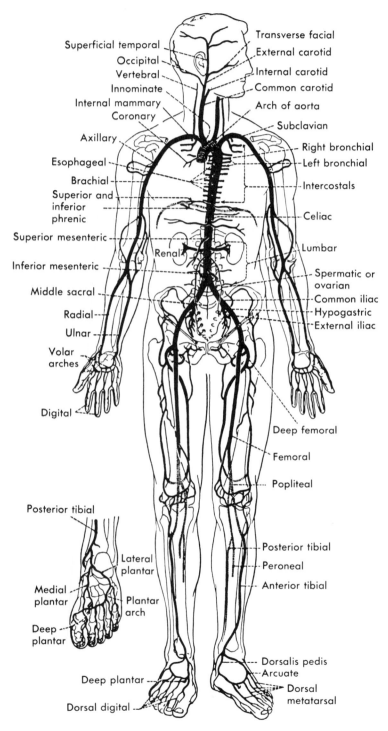

Fig. 59. Human arterial system. (From Millard, N. D., King, B. G., and Showers, M. J.: Human anatomy and physiology, Philadelphia, 1956, W. B. Saunders Co.)

way between its base and the place where it passes through the body wall.

4. Cut the **left** and **right common carotid arteries**, which branch from the **innominate vein** within the body cavity.

5. Cut the **left subclavian artery** and the small tributaries that enter its base.

6. Cut the **dorsal aorta** below the aortic arch or behind the heart and also cut the pulmonary arteries and veins.

7. Lift up the vessels that have been cut anterior to the heart and carefully pull the heart and its attached vessels away from the lower part of the trachea, bronchi, and base of the lungs, leaving them in place. Now the heart can be examined on all sides.

DISSECTION OF RIGHT SIDE OF HEART (Fig. 60)

This dissection will be done in the same order and direction as the flow of the blood.

1. **First step:** With the scissors clip a small hole in the **superior vena cava** and in the **inferior vena cava**, close to their place of entrance into the heart. Insert a probe in each of the clipped openings and push them into the **right atrium**, where they will touch one another. Cut the ventral walls of the blood vessels and the right atrium with the scissors, following close to the probes, as indicated by the broken line in the drawing of the ventral right lateral view of the heart (Fig. 60). Remove the injecting material.

2. **Second step:** Place the end of a probe in the **right atrium** and push it down into the **right ventricle**. Now cut the ventral wall of the latter open by cutting down along the side of the probe to the lower part of the right ventricle. This is shown in the drawing by a broken line. Remove the latex or other injecting material from the right ventricle and see the fleshy columns, or **trabeculae carneae**, on the inside of the wall. The blood leaves the **right ventricle**

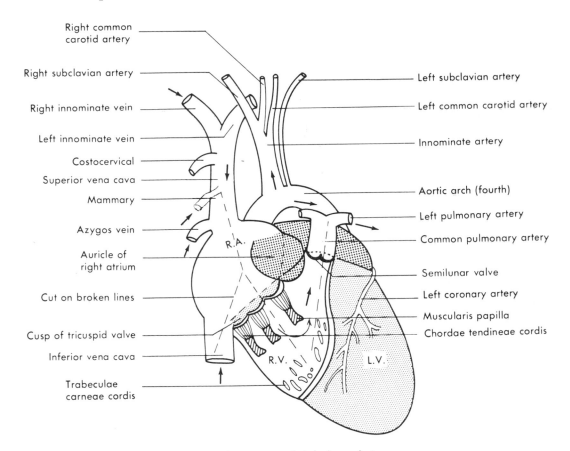

Fig. 60. Heart, ventral-right lateral view.

past the bicuspid or semilunar valves through the **common pulmonary artery** on its way to the lungs, past the **semilunar valves.** This blood vessel extends upward from the **right ventral** close to the ventral surface of the heart and between the two atria, where it divides into **right** and **left pulmonary arteries.**

3. **Third step:** By exercising some care you can push the probe into the common **pulmonary artery** from the inside of the **right ventricle.** When this has been done, cut with the scissors, following the probe as a guide, up to a point where the pulmonary artery divides to carry impure blood to each lung. Now the **tricuspid valves** between the right atrium and right ventricle can be seen better. There are three **cusps,** or **flaps,** and each is supported by fine fi-

bers, or **chordae tendineae,** and **one papillary muscle.** The **semilunar valves** can also be seen between the right ventricle and the common pulmonary artery. There are two earlike projections, or **auricular appendages,** one on the ventral wall of each atrium. These are usually somewhat more wrinkled and darker than the other parts of the heart. The **common pulmonary artery** extends between the right and left earlike projections and divides, sending a blood vessel to each lung. The small **ligamentum arteriosum** extends from the base of the **left pulmonary artery** to the **aortic arch** of the dorsal aorta, as shown in Fig. 61. This ligament is the remnant of the distal end of the left embryonic **sixth aortic arch,** which closed following birth, thus forcing all blood from the right ventricle to go to

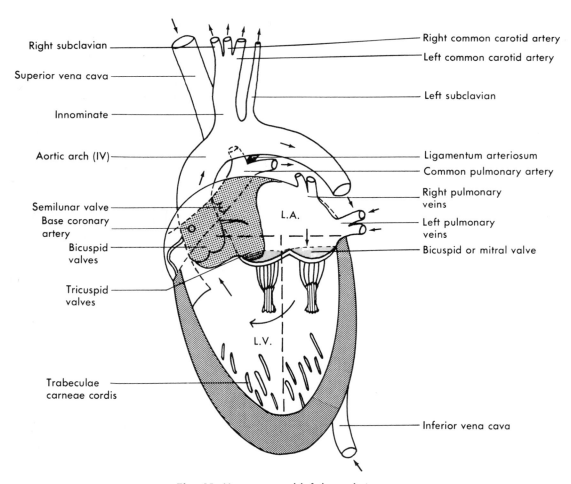

Fig. 61. Heart, ventral-left lateral view.

the lungs to be oxygenated. Add colored arrows to indicate purity and direction of flow in these parts.

DISSECTION OF LEFT SIDE OF HEART (Fig. 61)

1. **First step:** Cut transversely with the scissors through the ventral wall of the left atrium and extend the cut through the **left auricular appendage,** a dark, earlike projection, as indicated by the broken line in the drawing. Remove any injecting material.

2. **Second step:** Insert a probe into the left atrium, push it down into the left ventricle, and extend the cut past the bicuspid valves with the scissors down to the very tip end of the cavity as indicated by the broken line in Fig. 61. Dig and wash out the contents of the left ventricle and the left atrium and dry with paper towels. Now you should be able to probe from the inside of the left atrium and find the openings of the right and left **pulmonary veins,** which bring oxygenated blood from the lungs into the left atrium.

Between the left atrium and left ventricle you may now find the **bicuspid,** or **mitral, valves.** Observe the relative thickness of the walls of each of the four cavities of the heart.

3. **Third step:** If the base of the dorsal aorta has been well injected with latex, the vessels may be split open with the scissors and the latex removed intact. The latex often pushes down against the **semilunar valves,** leaving a good impression of them and of the bases of the **coronary arteries** immediately above (Fig. 61). After the base of the aorta has been split above these valves, you can push a probe past the valves into the left ventricle. The base of the dorsal aorta is the **fourth,** or **sytemic, aortic arch** of the left side.

Place the end of your thumb in the **right atrium** and the forefinger of the same hand in the **left atrium.** Now try to rub the ends of the thumb and finger together and thus find the thinnest place in the septum separating the two atria. Hold this up between your eyes and the light, and you will see a very thin spot. This is the **fossa ovale** and

represents the place where the opening between the two atria existed during embryonic development. This opening was called the **foramen ovale,** and it closed soon after birth to form the **fossa ovale.** Sometimes in the human baby this opening does not close. Under these conditions all the blood does not go down into the right ventricle and to the lungs to be purified, but some passes through this opening; hence the baby does not have his blood sufficiently purified and is called a "blue baby" because of his dark or bluish color.

There are two kinds of circulation in respect to the heart: (1) **functional,** which is the flow of blood through the atria and ventricles, as just described, and (2) **nutritional,** which is the circulation of the blood through the coronary arteries and veins to supply the walls of the heart. The coronary arteries branch from the deep base of the aortic arch. These are probably injected red near the surface of the heart walls. The **coronary sinus,** into which several **coronary veins** from the wall of the heart empty, is covered with fat on the dorsal surface and in the groove separating the atria and ventricles, and enters the left posterior corner of the **right atrium.**

The embryological development of the cat and human hearts shows recapitulation quite nicely. In brief the heart passes through stages quite similar to an elasmobranch fish, having **one atrium** and **one ventricle;** later it has **two atria** and **one ventricle,** like a frog, and still later the ventricle divides and there are **two atria** and **two ventricles,** as in a bird or mammal.

In the typical vertebrate animal such as the dogfish shark (*Squalus acanthias*) or in the embryos of cat or man, there are structures representing six pairs of aortic arches. Their names and numbers are as follows: first aortic arch, mandibular; second aortic arch, hyoid; third aortic arch, common carotid; fourth aortic arch, systemic; fifth aortic arch, innominate; and sixth aortic arch, the pulmonary. In the adult of cat and man those remaining are the third (common carotid) on both sides; the fourth only on the left side, which is the base of the dorsal aorta, or the aortic arch; the sixth, with the proximal parts only, which are the bases of the pulmonary artery on each side. These remaining aortic arches have migrated from the pharyngeal region of the young embryo down into the thoracic cavity. All other parts of the six pairs of aortic arches of the embryo have disappeared in the adult cat and man. A case like this, which in the embryonic stages of a higher type animal some of its structures pass through stages similar to those of the adults of lower members of the same group, is called recapitulation. There are many such occurrences in the embryonic development of mammals. The branchial arches, the aortic arches, the pharyngeal pouches, the heart, the ear, and the kidneys are a few examples that are interpreted as showing recapitulation. Recapitulation supports the theory of evolution.

SOME DIFFERENCES IN THE ARTERIES OF CAT AND MAN

1. The left common carotid artery branches from the dorsal aorta in man, but in the cat it branches from the innominate artery.

2. The internal and external iliac arteries arise separately from the dorsal aorta in the cat, whereas there is a common iliac artery in man from which both arise.

3. In man the brachial artery divides into the radial and ulnar at the elbow, but in the cat it divides at about the middle of the humerus.

4. The dorsal aorta passes posteriorward in the cat and divides at the first sacral vertebra, whereas in man it divides at the fourth lumbar vertebra.

5. The internal carotid arteries are large in man, whereas they are relatively small in the cat.

6. In man the superior and inferior phrenic arteries supply the diaphragm, whereas in the cat there is only the inferior phrenic, which usually arises from the adrenal.

7. The deep femoral artery is relatively larger and more extensively developed in man than it is in the cat.

8. The erect position of man puts a much greater strain on the heart to pump the blood because of the pull of gravity.

9. Man is sometimes considered a mechanical misfit, partly because of the changes brought about largely by civilization. Some of these changes are inappropriate diet, contamination of air and water, lack of sufficient exercise when working in many industries, and houses that are often kept too warm.

REVIEW QUESTIONS ON ARTERIAL SYSTEM

1. How many pairs of aortic arches are represented in a typical vertebrate (embryo or adult) animal?

2. Give the names and numbers of the aortic arches that are present in an adult cat or in man? (Fig. 57)

3. State three places where blood or the plasma of blood is purified. (Figs. 47, A and 48)

4. Trace the blood as it passes from the left hind leg of a cat until it reaches the right ear and then returns to the right front leg. (Figs. 52, 53, and 57)

5. Trace carbon dioxide from the inferior mesenteric vein of the cat until it is eliminated from the body (Figs. 53, 55, 57, 61, 58, and 51)

6. Trace nitrogenous waste from the time it enters the right subclavian vein until it is eliminated from the body. (Figs. 53, 57, 60, 61, 57, 58, and 51)

7. What is the significance of the fossa ovale of the heart and how did it come about?

8. What is the "pulse" of man and where can it be demonstrated? (Use your own knowledge to answer.)

9. What is the significance of the ligamentum anteriosum? (Fig. 61)

10. Name and locate the bases of the blood vessels that supply nutriment to the heart. (Fig. 61)

11. Name three vestigial structures of cat or man.

12. Where do most red blood cells (erythrocytes) originate in the adult?

13. Explain to origin and function of the greater omentum.

14. What is chyle?

15. Name and locate three sets of valves in the heart. (Figs. 60 and 61)

16. Which aortic arch is retained from the embryo as a base of the aortic arch of the adult? (Fig. 57)

17. What are the names of the subclavian artery in the different regions of the foreleg? (Fig. 57)

18. Trace the circulation of the blood from the pancreas of Aselli and to the left ear and back to the hepatic artery. (Figs. 52, 53, 57, and 58)

19. Trace the blood from the saphena parva vein to the forearm and back to the hypogastric artery. (Figs. 52, 53, 60, 61, 57, and 58)

20. Explain the functional and the nutritional circulations of the lungs. (Figs. 52, 57, 60, and 61)

6

Pharyngeal region of the cat

PHARYNX AND LARYNX (Fig. 62)

In this exercise two students should work together, thus bisecting the head, pharynx, and part of the neck of one cat and leaving the other cat skull to be dissected in such a way as to remove its brain intact and permit a dorsal and a ventral view examination of the entire brain.

The pharynx in a vertebrate animal is that part of the alimentary canal into which gill clefts, or gill slits, open or from which pharyngeal pouches extend in the embryo. In order to examine the pharynx of the cat and its relationships it is best to bisect the entire skull and neck down to the upper parts of the trachea and esophagus. This is probably easiest done with a thin, sharp, fine-toothed saw. However, before the saw is used the softer parts should be cut with scissors and a sharp knife. Begin by cutting open the upper part of the trachea and larynx along its median ventral line. Continue this cut forward with the knife, cutting the base and entire tongue in half along its median sagittal plane.

Use the saw, beginning between the nasal bones and back between the frontal bones on the dorsal surface. As you saw deeper, be certain your saw strikes the cut made with scissors and knife on the ventral surface. The skull and neck can then be divided completely along the median sagittal plane with little difficulty, if care and some skill is exercised in keeping the saw in the exact median plane. Identify the following structures.

1. The **mouth,** or **buccal cavity,** develops by an infolding of the skin and is thus lined with epithelial ectoderm. The roof of the mouth is lined with thick transverse folds of mucosal epithelium known as rugae, which assist in swallowing as the dorsal surface of the tongue contacts them. The tongue is covered with several kinds of cornified papillae. The teeth are believed to be homologous with placoid scales.

2. The **tongue** forms a part of the floor of the mouth and pharynx. It arises beneath the pharynx and pushes forward into the mouth during embryonic development. Several muscles contribute to its formation. On the base of the **tongue** is a small pit, the **foramen cecum,** which marks the place where the **thyroid gland** passed in its embryonic migration to its position in the adult, below the laryngeal cartilages.

3. The **external nares** and **nasal chambers,** like the mouth, are lined with ectoderm, since they push in from the outside and join the pharynx by the internal apertures, or **choanae.** The maxillary and palatine bones form the **hard palate,** which separates the mouth and nasal cavities. The **turbinate bones** push into each nasal cavity from the lateral side of each nasal chamber and are parts of the ethmoid and maxillary bones. The **soft palate** is posterior to the **hard palate,** and in man there is a fingerlike process that hangs down from its center known as the **uvula.** This is absent in the cat.

4. Two air cells, or air sinuses, are above

153

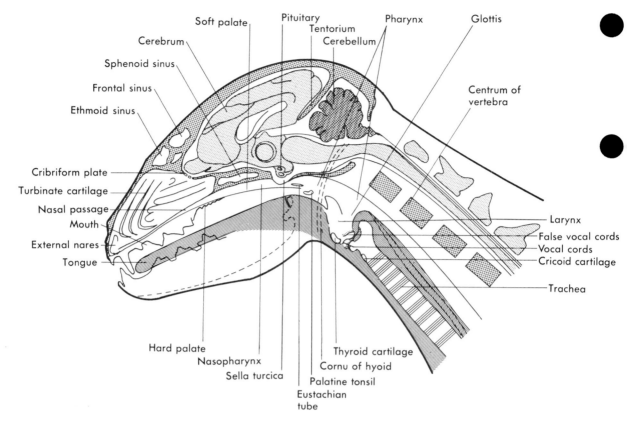

Fig. 62. Pharynx and larynx, median sagittal view.

the **cribriform plate** and nasal chambers. The more anterior is the **ethmoid sinus,** and the posterior is the **frontal sinus.** These drain into the nasal chamber in mammals, but the erect position of man's body makes this difficult and is one of the factors involved in sinus trouble. The third air space is the **sphenoid sinus** within the sphenoid bone anterior to the sella turcica.

5. The cranial cavity contains the brain. The **cerebrum** and **cerebellum** are partially separated by the **tentorium** in the cat. This is an ossified portion of the dura mater that forms extensions on the parietal bones. It is absent in man. In the cranial floor is a depression, the sella turcica, that contains the **pituitary gland.** The membranes covering the brain are collectively known as the **meninges.** The outer is the dura mater; the middle is the arachnoid; and the inner is the pia mater.

6. The **eustachian tube** is a passageway from the **pharynx** to the vestibule of the

middle ear. It represents the vestigial remains of the inner portion of the first gill cleft. The **opening of the eustachian tube** into the pharynx is just posterior to the **hamular process** of the **sphenoid bone.** The opening appears to be in the lateral wall of the nasal chamber, because in the cat the soft palate grows posteriorward and divides the anterior part of the pharynx into a **nasal** and a **stomodeal portion.**

7. The **palatine tonsil** is located in a small depression in the lateral wall of the **pharynx** and is about the size of a grain of rice. Part of it represents the endodermal lining of the second **pharyngeal pouch,** or gill cleft. This gland is usually removed in a **tonsilectomy** in man. There are two other kinds of tonsils, the **pharyngeal,** or **adenoids,** and the **lingual.** The former are in the middorsal portion of the pharynx close to the internal apertures, or nares, and in man, when the pharyngeal tonsils enlarge, the internal nares are constricted or

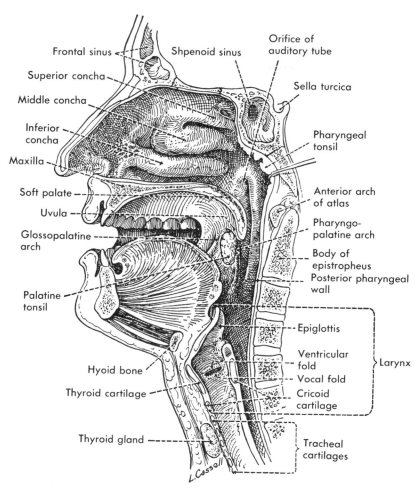

Fig. 63. Sagittal section through the human mouth, larynx, pharynx, and nasal cavity. (From Millard, N. D., King, B. G., and Showers, M. J.: Human anatomy and physiology, Philadelphia, 1956, W. B. Saunders Co.)

closed. The **lingual tonsils** are imbedded in the lateral edges of the posterior part of the tongue. The **pharyngeal** and **lingual tonsils** are small, hence we identify only the palatine tonsils in gross dissection.

8. The **larynx**, or **voice box** (Figs. 34, C and 62), is also called the **Adam's apple** in man and lies ventral to the posterior portion of the **pharynx**; the cavities of the two are connected by the **glottis**. A fold of cartilage, the **epiglottis**, guards this opening and causes it to become closed, so that food passes over the opening when swallowing. There are two large cartilages that support and are embedded in the walls of the larynx, the **thyroid**, which is the larger, and the **cricoid** (see Fig. 34, A to C). Feel your

own throat and larynx. Find the notch on the upper edge of the thyroid cartilage. Push the end of your finger up and feel the hyoid cartilage or bone. Below the broad thyroid cartilage there is no hard tissue until you reach the cricoid cartilage. The cornu of the **hyoid bone** or cartilage consists of several sections and is embedded in the lateral wall and floor of the region immediately anterior to the larynx proper and, strictly speaking, is not a part of the larynx but it more closely associated with the base of the tongue. The **cornu of the hyoid** is shown as two broken lines in Fig. 62 as a succession of parts extending up to the region of the auditory bulla. There are also some smaller cartilages, the **arytenoid**,

155

cuneiform, and **corniculate,** that are not to be identified at this time. These cartilages are homologous with the **branchial arches** that support the gills in the fish. Also, in the higher forms such as the cat and man, the **malleus, incus,** and **stapes,** or bones of the middle ear, are derived from the branchial arches.

9. Within the larynx are membranous folds, the **vocal cords,** which extend toward the center of the lumen and leave a narrow slit, the edges of which vibrate and produce sound waves. The **false vocal cords** are thickenings closer to the glottis, anterior and above the true vocal cords, and are believed to enable the cat to "purr."

Indicate on Fig. 62 the route taken in the passage of food by **green arrows** and the passage of air by **blue arrows.**

10. Examine the **trachea, bronchi,** and **bronchioli** (Fig. 34, *C*). Cut the tracheal tube open longitudinally and examine its cartilaginous rings; examine also the bronchi and bronchioli. How do they differ? The **esophagus** lies between the trachea and the lower **cervical vertebrae.** Compare Figs. 62 and 63. What are the principal differences and similarities?

REVIEW QUESTIONS ON PHARYNX, LARYNX, AND SALIVARY GLANDS

1. Name the openings that lead into or away from the pharynx (Fig. 62)

2. Name the different structures through which air passes when a cat breathes. (Figs. 47, B and 62)

3. Name the different structures, in order, through which food passes in reaching the pyloric cecum and name the digestive secretions receievd at each place. (Fig. 47, B)

4. Hold your nose and swallow; now explain the cause of the sensation you get in your ears. (To answer rely on your own judgment; Figs. 64 and 65)

5. Name four cartilages that lie in the region of the larynx. (Figs. 34, A and 62)

6. Name the three salivary glands and their respective ducts. (Fig. 34, B)

7. Name the larger arteries and veins that lie close to the salivary glands. (Figs. 34, B, 52, and 54)

8. State three reasons why man has sometimes been called a mechanical misfit.

9. Name and locate the three kinds of tonsils. (Fig. 62)

10. Where is the thyroid gland located in reference to the cartilages of the larynx? (Fig. 34, C)

11. When a person swallows, what is the relationship between the passage through which the food goes and the larynx? (Fig. 62)

12. What is the eustachian tube called in the early embryo? (Fig. 65)

13. What is the location and significance of the cribiform plate?

14. Give the technical name and the principal structure of the "Adam's apple". (Fig. 62)

15. What would you say are the principal differences in the respiratory tracts shown in Figs. 62 and 63.

16. Name the structures through which food passes from the mouth to the stomach. (Figs. 62 and 63)

17. Name the structures through which air passes from the external nares to the lungs in the cat and in man. (Figs. 62 and 63)

18. Compare the air sinuses in the cat and in man. (Figs. 62 and 63)

19. What is the main function of the hepatic portal system? (Figs. 53 to 55)

20. Name the principal structures of each of the three main parts of the ear. (Fig. 65)

DISSECTION OF EAR (Figs. 64 and 65)

Remove the skin from the entire skull, if this has not been done. The two functions of the ear are (a) **equilibrium** and (b) **hearing**. There are three principal parts of the ear of the cat—external, middle, and inner. Each is different in embryological origin. Each of these parts and their subdivisions will now be discussed.

1. The **external ear** consists of the **pinna**, or **concha**, which projects from the surface of the head. It is composed of elastic cartilage derived embryologically from the first two **visceral arches** and is covered with skin. The ear of the cat is pointed at the end. If you feel the edge of the upper posterior cartilage portion of **your own ear**, you will probably find a thickening of cartilage. The facts of embryological development show that this thickening is comparable with the top end of a pointed ear that is folded over.

Cut off the left **pinna** close to the skull bones of the cat. The **external auditory meatus** is the hole or opening in the side of the head above the **auditory**, or **tympanic, bulla**. Observe the cartilage that lines the bony cavity. The **skin ectoderm** covering the **pinna** continues and lines the cavity and near its inner end gives rise to the **ceruminous**, or **wax, glands**, which are too small to be seen in ordinary dissection. Cut this cartilage and bone away until the meatus enlarges and the **eardrum**, or **tympanic membrane**, can be seen. It arises by the skin ectoderm, infolding to form the lining of the meatus with the endoderm lining from the pharynx pushed up through the eustachian tube, which lines the middle ear vestibule and forms the **inner layer** of the tympanic membrane, or eardrum.

2. The **middle ear** consists of the vestibule or cavity, which contains the malleus, incus, and stapes and also the inner half of the tympanum. The vestibule and eustachian tube represent the inner portion of the first embryonic pharyngeal pouch or gill cleft. Find the opening of the eustachian tube (Fig. 62) in the lateral wall of the pharynx partly surrounded by the hamular process of the sphenoid bone, which can be felt by the tip end of the finger.

The edge of the opening is often thickened and white in color. Insert a fine wire or probe into the opening and push it up into the eustachian tube. Now cut away the bone covering the wire or probe, holding the scalpel in a horizontal position. The eustachian tube and vestibule permits the air pressure to be equalized on the two sides of the eardrum, which then vibrates more easily. If you hold your own nose and swallow, you increase the air pressure from the pharynx up through the eustachian tube against the eardrum; it does not vibrate so easily, and you do not hear so well.

The bones of the middle ear, the **malleus, incus,** and **stapes,** are important in the process of hearing, since they transmit the stimulus produced by the sound waves. They are difficult to expose in dissecting because they are surrounded by hard bone, are small, and are easily damaged. Cut away the bone at the **tympanum** and loosen the anterior half of the tympanum. The **malleus** can be seen with one end on the inner side of the eardrum (Fig. 65), with the large end posterior to the membrane, where it articulates with the **incus.** The incus in turn articulates with the **stapes.** Now cut away the posterior wall of the tympanum and locate the incus and the stapes. Fine folds of the lining of the vestibule support these bones, therefore it is somewhat difficult to identify them. If you succeed in removing these three bones intact, you may consider yourself skillful and perhaps lucky also. They are easier to dissect intact on a dry skull.

These ear bones originate from the **visceral,** or **branchial, arches** of the embryo, the malleus and incus from the **mandibular,** or **first,** and the stapes from the **hyoid arch,** or the second. Now you can pass a fine wire up through the eustachian tube, the vestibule, past the tympanum, and out the remainder of the external auditory meatus.

Cut away the ventral wall of the tympanic, or auditory bulla, and expose its cavity. The outline of the cavity varies with the depth at which it is cut. The oval thickened area of the dorsolateral wall of the bulla contains the parts of the **inner ear** within the petrosal part of the tem-

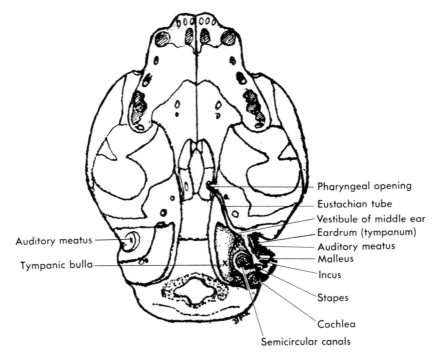

Auditory meatus

Tympanic bulla

Pharyngeal opening

Eustachian tube

Vestibule of middle ear

Eardrum (tympanum)

Auditory meatus

Malleus

Incus

Stapes

Cochlea

Semicircular canals

Fig. 64

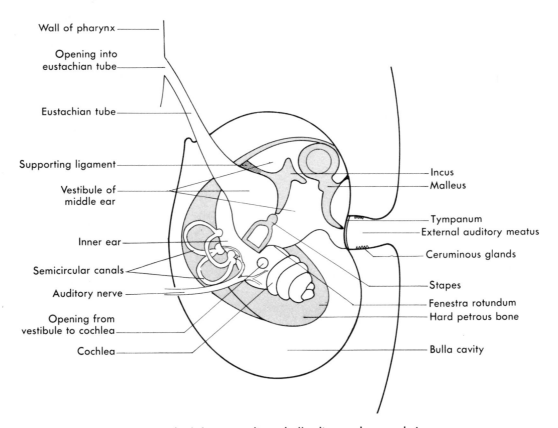

Wall of pharynx

Opening into eustachian tube

Eustachian tube

Supporting ligament

Vestibule of middle ear

Inner ear

Semicircular canals

Auditory nerve

Opening from vestibule to cochlea

Cochlea

Incus

Malleus

Tympanum

External auditory meatus

Ceruminous glands

Stapes

Fenestra rotundum

Hard petrous bone

Bulla cavity

Fig. 65. The left ear, auditory bulla dissected, ventral view.

poral bone. A small opening in the dorso-lateral wall of the bulla connects with the vestibule. It is believed that the tympanic bulla amplifies sound much the same as the body of a violin, cello, or bass viol. The bulla probably accounts in part for the greater keenness in hearing in the cat than that in man, who has no bulla.

3. The **inner ear** is composed of the **semicircular canals,** the **cochlea,** the **sacculus,** and the **utriculus.** All of these parts are embedded in the **petrous part of the temporal bone,** which is the hardest bone in the body. In fact it is so hard that it is quite difficult to break. It is endochondral, or preformed in cartilage, in its development. Cut or break away parts of the **petrous bone** as best you can, and you may be lucky enough to see parts of the cavities of the **semicircular canals** and **cochlea.** A hand lens is usually necessary in identifying these parts. In each ear there are three semicircular canals, which lie in different planes, and when the animal changes position, the enclosed lymph shifts and stimulates the nerve endings differently in the ampullae. Because of this stimulus on the nerve endings in the ampullae, the animal is able to keep its balance, or **equilibrium.** The **cochlea** is the spiral, or snail-shell–shaped, organ. The highly specialized cells within constitute the **organ of Corti.** These cells are specialized in such a manner that they respond to specific stimuli produced by a definite wavelength sound vibration. It is not definitely known how the ear functions. The sacculus and utriculus are small cavities with which the semicircular canals and the cochlea connect. All cavities of the inner ear, or labyrinth, are lined by the infolding of the skin ectoderm. For a time in the embryo they are connected with the skin by a tube known as the endolymphatic duct, as in the adult *Squalus acanthias* shark, but this constricts off in cat or man and the various parts differentiate.

The structures of the **inner ear** begin to form first in the embryos of cat and man. Then the **middle ear** forms, and lastly the **external ear** forms. This is the same order in which these parts form phylogenetically, or in the development of the group of ver-tebrates. In the **lowest fishes,** as in the dog-fish shark (*Squalus acanthias*), **only an inner ear forms.** In the amphibians, as in the frog, there is **only an inner** and a **middle ear** and no external ear. The middle ear bones are represented only by the columella and not separate malleus, incus, and stapes bones. When structures of a higher classed animal, such as the cat and man, pass through stages in their embryological development similar to those in the adults of lower members of the same group, it is designated as **recapitulation.** Recapitulation is interpreted as supporting the theory of **evolution.** Since the semicircular canals form first embryologically and phylogenetically, it is believed that they existed a long time before hearing was established.

In the cat there are **anterior** and **posterior auricular muscles** on the side of the skull by which the ear is moved. This enables the cat to catch the sound more easily and efficiently, which is important in avoiding enemies or in detecting other small animals to catch and use as food. These muscles are **vestigial** in man, but in nearly every schoolroom there is a young boy who can move or wiggle his ears for the entertainment of others. To what particular advantage it is to the boy is not known.

There are many rudimentary, degenerative, or vestigial organs in man that have little or no known function. Dr. Leslie B. Arey in the seventh edition of *Developmental Anatomy,* published by W. B. Saunders Co. in 1965, states that **"over 100** such organs have been listed for man, among such are the **coccyx, appendix, body hair, wisdom tooth,** and **ear muscles."** It is believed by most anatomists that an organ which is not used tends to degenerate and atrophy. This is the usual explanation of vestigial organs. Therefore it is believed that man, in his bodily structure, bears the indelible imprint of his lowly ancestry.

SOME DIFFERENCES IN PHARYNGEAL AND LARYNGEAL REGIONS OF CAT AND MAN

1. The soft palate of cat divides the anterior part of the pharynx into the nasal

and stomodeal portions. This does not occur in man.

2. The fingerlike projection on the edge of the soft palate in man is the uvula. This is absent in the cat.

3. The salivary glands are relatively much larger in the cat than those in man.

4. The submaxillary gland in the cat is closely associated with the parotid, whereas in man it lies below the mandible and is often called the submandibular gland.

5. The sublingual gland in the cat usually lies against the submaxillary, whereas in man it lies beneath the floor of the mouth under the tongue.

6. The palatine tonsils seem to be the only tonsils that are well developed in the cat, whereas man has three pairs of fairly large tonsils, the palatine, pharyngeal, and sublingual tonsils.

7. The hyoid bone in the cat is composed of a number of distinct segments, the basihyal, ceratohyal, epihyal, stylohyal, and tympanohyal, corresponding to the lesser cornu of man, whereas the thyrohyal of the cat is homologous with the entire greater cornu of man.

8. The lymph glands adjacent to the submaxillary and sublingual are relatively much larger in the cat than those in man.

9. The primary cause of the differences in the relationships of the skull and in the face of cat and man results from the enlargement of the cerebrum in man, which has pushed the skull dorsalward and the mouth, nose, and nasal chamber anteriorward or ventrally.

10. The size of the nose and nasal chamber has been relatively reduced in size in man, which is one of the factors causing a reduction in the keenness of smell.

11. The pharynx is normally held in a vertical position in man, whereas the pharynx of the cat is held at about a forty-five-degree angle or often in a horizontal position. It is generally recognized that the sinuses drain normally when the head is held in a horizontal position, therefore man is much more likely to have sinus trouble than a cat. Expressed in another way and supported by facts of embryology, the head of man appears to be much more distorted than that of the cat, largely because of the increase in size of the cerebrum.

REVIEW QUESTIONS ON EAR

1. State the two principal functions of the ear.

2. What is the difference between an aortic arch and a branchial arch? (Figs. 60 and 61)

3. What is the explanation of the area of thickened cartilage at the upper edge of the human ear?

4. Where do most of the white blood corpuscles, or leukocytes, originate?

5. Name the three bones of the middle ear. (Fig. 65)

6. What is believed to be the function of the tympanic, or auditory, bulla? (Figs. 4, 64, and 65)

7. Why does swallowing often interfere with the acuteness of man's hearing?

8. State the embryological origin of each of the bones of the middle ear. (Fig. 65)

9. Does air come up from the pharynx, eustachian tube, and vestibule of the middle ear, to the tympanic membrane? If so, what is the result?

10. Why are the bones of the middle ear sometimes called the hammer, anvil, and stirrup? (Fig. 65)

11. Due to the complexity of the cavities of the inner ear, what is the general name of all the cavities?

12. What is the function of the semicircular canals?

13. What primitive germ layer lines each of the cavities of the inner ear?

14. What is the nature of the petrous bone?

15. What part of the ear is the most essential organ of hearing? (Fig. 65)

16. Within what part of the temporal bone is the organ of Corti?

17. Name five senses of cat or man. (Use your own judgment.)

18. Hold your nose and swallow. Air is forced from the pharynx up the eustachian tube against the tympanum, or eardrum, and you get the sensation. Can you hear well during the process? Why?

19. In what part of the ear are the physical stimuli transferred or transformed into nervous stimuli, or in other words, where are the receptive ends of the auditory nerve located? (Fig. 65)

20. Trace the stimulus produced by sound waves entering the auditory meatus until it reaches the brain. (Fig. 65)

7

Brain of the cat

MEDIAN SAGITTAL SECTION OF BRAIN (Fig. 66)

Carefully remove the left half of the brain from the skull, previously examined. Embryology shows that the brain is really the enlarged end of the spinal cord. There are five principal parts, or lobes, that constitute the brain, and there are several parts in each lobe. Each of these lobes will be considered, but only the parts of each that may be seen in the median sagittal section will be mentioned.

1. The **cerebrum (telencephalon)** is the most anterior of the lobes and occupies the largest portion of the cranial cavity. It is covered by the frontal and parietal bones and rests on the diencephalon and mesencephalon. The following structures are some of the parts of the cerebrum that may be seen.

(a) The convolutions consist of ridges, or **gyri,** and grooves, or **sulci.**

(b) The **olfactory bulbs (rhinencephalon)** lie against the cribriform plate, and some of the small olfactory nerve fibers may be seen entering the foramina if the lobe is gently pushed back.

(c) The **corpus callosum** may be identified as follows. Each hemisphere of the cerebrum contains a cavity, the paracele. The **corpus callosum** forms the dense white roof of this cavity near the median plane. This is composed of many nerve fibers extending from one hemisphere to the other. Below the paracele is the **fornix,** which is

also composed of transverse nerve fibers closely packed together.

(d) The **septum pellucidum** is a thin, double partition that lies in a vertical position in the median plane and separates the two paraceles, or cavities, of two hemispheres of the cerebrum.

2. The **lower thalamic region (diencephalon)** is the second main lobe of the brain and is composed of the following parts.

(a) The **intermediate commissure** appears as a solid, circular area extending transversely near the center of the cavity of the **diacele,** or **third ventricle.** The intermediate commissure also is composed of many nerve fibers.

(b) The **epiphysis (pineal gland,** pineal body, or vestigial third eye) is small and dorsal to the intermediate commissure. It constitutes a part of the dorsal wall, or roof of the third ventricle. In the early embryological development the **epiphysis** is actually on the dorsal surface of the brain, but the **cerebrum** enlarges and folds back, covering the epiphysis, which is still really on the dorsal surface of the brain.

(c) The **infundibulum** is a ventral projection from the floor of the diencephalon. It is the posterior portion of the pituitary, or hypophysis, which lies in the sella turcica of the sphenoid bone. The anterior portion of the pituitary arises from the roof of the stomodeum, or mouth, and is known as **Rathke's pouch.**

(d) The **optic chiasma** is anterior to the

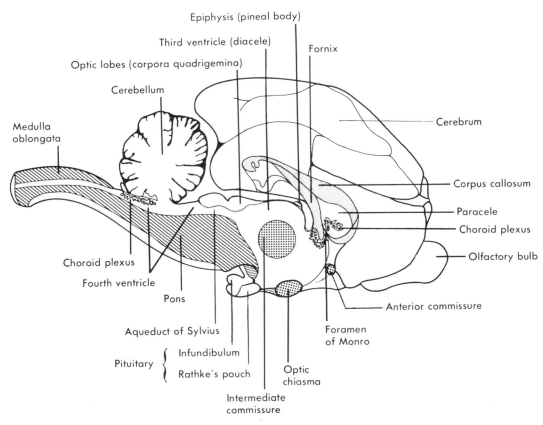

Fig. 66. Brain, median sagittal view.

pituitary and is composed of the optic nerve fibers, most of which cross one another in this area.

(e) The **tuber cinereum** is a small rounded area between the optic chiasma and the base of the pituitary gland to which the infundibulum is attached.

(f) The **foramen of Monro** is the opening that connects the cavity of the diencephalon (the **diacele,** or **third ventricle**) with each paracele of each hemisphere of the cerebrum. The **choroid plexus** is an infolded part of the roof of the diacele extending through the **foramen of Monro** into each paracele. It is dark because of the blood it contains. This infolding furnishes a good blood supply to the inside of the cerebrum.

3. The **optic lobes** (mesencephalon) appear in each half of the brain as two lobes, one behind the other, posterior to the pineal gland. In mammals there are four of these lobes; hence they are also given the name **corpora quadrigemina.** The anterior pair

constitutes a relay center for sight and the posterior pair, a center for hearing. The cavity below these lobes is very small and is known as the **iter,** or **aqueduct of Sylvius.**

4. The **cerebellum** (metencephalon), as it lies in the skull, is partially separated from the cerebrum by the tentorium, which is really an ossified portion of the dura mater. When cut in median sagittal section, the cerebellum shows a characteristic branching structure, and since it somewhat resembles a tree, it is called the arbor vitae. The cavity of the cerebellum is the **fourth ventricle,** and it also extends posteriorly into the medulla oblongata. The floor of the fourth ventricle is thick and consists of the **pons.**

5. Most of the roof of the **medulla oblongata** (myelencephalon) is very thin and often is destroyed in dissecting before being identified. A part of the roof folds into the fourth ventricle, forming a **choroid plexus,** which extends to the inner surface

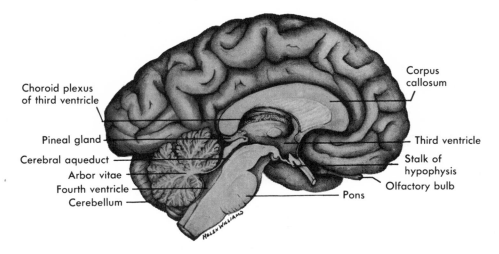

Choroid plexus
of third ventricle

Corpus
callosum

Pineal gland

Cerebral aqueduct

Arbor vitae

Fourth ventricle

Cerebellum

Third ventricle

Stalk of
hypophysis

Olfactory bulb

Pons

Fig. 67. Sagittal section through the midline of the human brain, showing the medial surface of the left half. (From Francis, C. C., and Farrell, G. L.: Integrated anatomy and physiology, St. Louis, 1957, The C. V. Mosby Co.)

of the cerebellum and brings blood to it. The lateral walls are thicker, and the floor is thickest of all. The posterior limit of the medulla is at the foramen magnum of the skull, where it joins the spinal cord. So far as position and structure are concerned, the medulla is a transition between the brain proper and the spinal cord. Show different lobes of the brain in different colors as follows: 1, blue; 2, red; 3, yellow; 4, green; 5, orange.

Compare Figs. 66 and 67. Note five similarities and five differences.

DORSAL VIEW OF BRAIN (Fig. 68)

By having the students work in pairs on the pharynx and the median view of the brain, as previously stated, we now have an intact skull from which the entire brain may be removed. It is better not to cut the head from the body until the dorsal skull bones have been removed.

A good pair of bone shears is needed for removing the bones of the roof of the skull in order to remove the brain intact. Begin at the anterior limits of the frontal bones and cut through into the frontal sinuses. Continue clipping small pieces of bone away without injuring the brain until the roof is entirely removed. If the brain is too soft, the entire skull with the brain should be hardened in formalin unless disintegration has gone too far.

Remove the hardened brain from the skull by first lifting up the medulla, then the cerebellum; lift forward until the entire brain is loosened and removed. Special care must be exercised so as not to injure the pituitary gland. Reexamine Fig. 66 (the right half of the brain) to determine how to cut down with a scalpel behind and under the pituitary so as to remove it uninjured.

The **meninges** are the covering membranes of the brain. They will be considered, beginning with the outer one.

1. The **dura mater** was previously mentioned in discussing the cerebellum. Mostly it lies against the bones, but part of it is ossified to form the tentorium in the cat, but not so in man.

2. The **arachnoid** is the middle layer and contains the blood vessels.

3. The **pia mater,** or inner layer of the meninges, may be seen as the thin membrane that dips down into the sulci, or grooves, of the convolutions of the brain. Next, examine the dorsal view of the cerebrum. The **great longitudinal, or median, fissure** separates the two hemispheres; each hemisphere has three longitudinal folds, or gyri, on its dorsal surface, which are separated from one another by longitudinal grooves, or sulci. The three principal gyri on each half of the brain are named, beginning near the median line, as the (a) **marginal,** (b) **suprasylvius,** and (c) **ectosyl-**

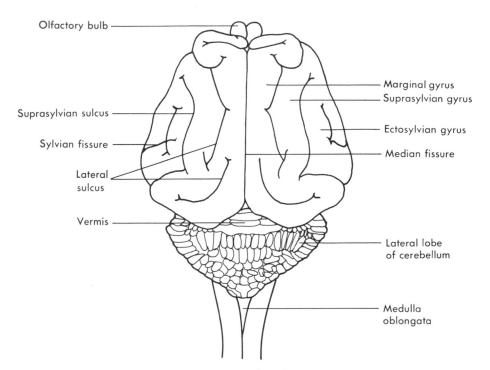

Fig. 68. Brain, dorsal view.

Labels on figure:
Olfactory bulb
Suprasylvian sulcus
Sylvian fissure
Lateral sulcus
Vermis
Marginal gyrus
Suprasylvian gyrus
Ectosylvian gyrus
Median fissure
Lateral lobe of cerebellum
Medulla oblongata

vius. The four principal sulci, or grooves, on each half are named from the median fissure laterally as the (a) **lateral,** which is in two parts, the posterior portion turning laterally near the cerebellum, (b) **suprasylvian,** which turns laterally near each end, (c) **cruciate sulcus,** which extends transversely on each side near the olfactory bulb and begins at the median fissure, and (d) **sylvian fissure,** which is at the greatest width of the cerebrum as it comes to the dorsal surface.

The **diencephalon** and the **mesencephalon** are comparatively small in the cat and have been covered by the enlargement and growth of the posterior portion of the cerebrum, and hence they are not seen in the dorsal view.

The **metencephalon** (cerebellum) is characterized by having many small irregular folds, or gyri. These are arranged in three principal groups. The median portion is the **vermis,** which has a **lateral lobe,** or **cerebellar hemisphere,** on each side.

The myelencephalon (medulla oblongata) may be seen from the dorsal view as the rapidly narrowing structure projecting from under the posterior fold of the cerebellum and is continuous with the spinal cord.

Use colors comparable with those in previous drawings for each of the lobes shown.

VENTRAL VIEW OF BRAIN (Fig. 69)

The ventral view of the cat brain appears more complex than the dorsal. This is largely because the brainstem is exposed better with the bases of the cranial nerves attached to it.

Each **olfactory bulb** and its **tract** may now me observed with its **lateral roots.** The **cranial nerve I** (**olfactory tract**) fibers extend forward from each olfactory bulb through the cribriform plate and end on the turbinate bones. The **postrhinal fissure** may be traced along the lateral side of each **olfactory bulb** to the lateral surface, where is is usually continuous with the **sylvian fissure.** The crossing of the **cranial nerve II** (**optic**) fibers forms the **optic chiasma.** The **pituitary body,** or **hypophysis,** is the knob-like projection immediately posterior to the chiasma; dorsal to it is the **tuber cinereum.** The **mammillary bodies** lie caudad to the

168

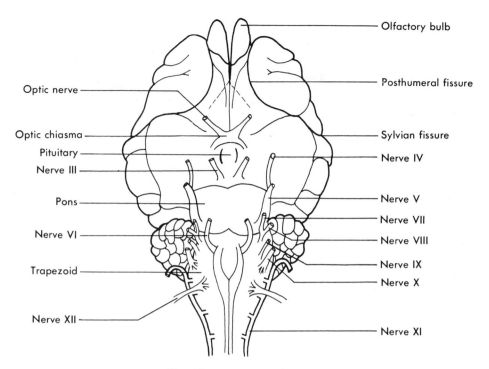

Fig. 69. Brain, ventral view.

tuber cinereum. **Cranial nerve III (motor oculus)** arises near the midventral line posterior to the mammillary bodies. Lateral to the tuber cinereum, the mammillary bodies, and the third cranial nerve, there is a large, rather oval swelling. This is the **pyriform lobe** of the cerebrum. On each side of the mammillary bodies and the pyriform lobe is a depressed area that it a part of the **peduncle** of the cerebrum. Near its lateral limit the base of **cranial nerve IV (pathetic** or **trochlear)** may be seen.

Farther posterior near the median area is a pair of transverse enlargement, the **pons,** which are tracts, or association fibers, of the cerebellum. Near the caudal edge of the pons are the bases of three cranial nerves; the larger and most anterior is **nerve V (trigeminal).** Behind its base is **nerve VII (facial),** and posterior to it is the root of **nerve VIII (auditory).** The base of **nerve VI (abducens)** lies between the base of **nerve VIII (auditory)** and the midventral line. It is small, easily mutilated, and often is difficult to locate. The **trapezoid body** lies on each side between the

bases of the abducens and auditory nerves, and the **anterior pyramids** lie between the bases of the two abducens nerves and extend as longitudinal swellings on the ventral surface of the medulla on each side of the median ventral line.

Nerve IX (glossopharyngeal) and **nerve X (vagus)** arise near the lateral surface of the medulla slightly posterior to the eighth. **Nerve XI (spinal accessory)** arises from several fibers along the lateral edge of the medulla and extends from the brain only slightly behind the base of the tenth. **Nerve XII (hypoglossal)** arises on the ventral surface of the medulla and appears at its base very much the same as the first cervical nerve. The floor of the embryonic brain (brainstem) with the bases of the cranial nerves changes least in development. The dorsal and lateral walls thicken most, particularly those of the first and fourth lobes. The principal bending of the brain is correlated with the erect position of man.

Color parts of the brain the same as in previous drawings.

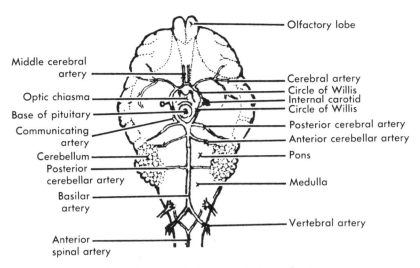

Fig. 70. Ventral view of arteries of brain.

ARTERIAL SUPPLY TO VENTRAL SURFACE OF BRAIN (Fig. 70)

Several arteries may be seen on the ventral surface of the well-injected brain. These are to be identified on your specimen and colored red on Fig. 70.

The **vertebral artery** extends forward on each side along the neck, passing through a series of transverse foramina in the transverse processes of the cervical vertebrae. They converge, passing through the foramen magnum, and unite into the **basilar artery** (Fig. 57). The basilar artery extends forward against the median ventral surface of the **medulla** and the **pons**. Upon reaching the **mammillary bodies** it divides and passes on each side of the bases of the **hypophysis,** or **pituitary,** and the **optic chiasma,** forming the **circle of Willis.**

The pituitary is considered the **master endocrinal gland,** since it controls the secretions of several hormone-producing glands. The thyroid, parathyroid, pancreas, adrenal, ovaries, and testes are other endocrinal glands. Along the course of the median basilar artery the pituitary gives off **posterior inferior cerebellar arteries** to the posteroventral part of the cerebellum and, more anteriorly, a pair of small **anterior cerebellar arteries** that pass dorsally to the trigeminal nerve to supply the **cerebellum.**

At the anterior end of the median basilar artery a pair of larger arteries, the **posterior cerebral arteries,** are given off. The circle of Willis receives the anterior extremity of the **internal carotid artery** on each side and passes anteriorly to the chiasma, where it forms a complete circle and gives off a pair of large **middle cerebral arteries** to supply much of the ventral surface of the cerebrum. **Smaller arteries** branch from near the median line to extend to the bases of the **olfactory lobes.** The vertebral and the internal carotid arteries are the main supply of blood to the brain.

On each side of the pituitary a small **communicating artery** unites the posterior cerebral and the internal carotid arteries. The small **anterior spinal artery** lies along the midventral line of the spinal cord and, upon entering the skull through the foramen magnum, branches to supply the medulla and the ventral cerebellar area. The latter portion is known as the posterior inferior cerebellar artery, and it anastomoses with the small branches of the basilar artery.

SOME DIFFERENCES IN BRAINS OF CAT AND MAN

1. The cerebrum of man is relatively larger and has many more complex convolutions than that of the cat.

2. The brain of man is bent more than that of the cat.

3. The olfactory bulbs in the cat are rel-

atively larger and more protruding than those in man.

4. The walls of the cerebrum and cerebellum in man are relatively thicker than they are in the cat, and they contain more cells and synapses.

5. The hemispheres of the cerebellum are more definitely differentiated from the central vermis in man than they are in the cat.

6. In man the enlarged cerebral lobes of the brain grow over and cover the olfactory bulbs and the cerebellum. This does not occur in the cat.

7. The median commissure in the third ventricle of the cat is relatively larger than that in man.

REVIEW QUESTIONS ON BRAIN

1. Give the common and scientific names of each of the five lobes of the cat brain.

2. From what view may the five main parts of the cat brain be seen the best? (Fig. 66)

3. Name the bones of the skull that help form the cranial cavity. (Fig. 6)

4. Name the three layers of the meninges.

5. What constitutes the brainstem, and what are the general relationships of the cranial nerves to it? (Fig. 69)

6. What is the circle of Willis? (Fig. 70)

7. Name the cavities of the brain and state the location of each.

8. Name the cranial nerves and state the location where each arises from the brainstem. (Fig. 69)

9. Trace the stimulus of a sound wave that strikes the pinna until it reaches the brain.

10. List, in order, the names of the twelve pairs of cranial nerves. (Fig. 69)

11. What specific anatomic adaptation does a cat have for life in the wild?

12. What are the principal differences in the cat and human brain? (Figs. 66 and 67)

13. What are sulci? Name three. (Fig. 68)

14. What are gyri? (Fig. 68)

15. Which two arteries unite to form the basal artery? (Fig. 70)

16. How is the blood circulation correlated with respiration?

17. What endocrinal gland is on the ventral side of the diencephalon? (Fig. 69)

18. Which lobes of the brain have the thinnest dorsal walls? (Fig. 66)

19. Explain and locate two choroid plexuses. (Fig. 66)

20. What are the paraceles?

21. What is the foramen of Monro, and what passes through it?

8

Spinal cord and peripheral nerves of the cat

INTRODUCTION

Typically, there is one pair of nerves for each vertebra of the spinal column, with dorsal and ventral roots, branches on each side from the spinal cord. Each nerve thus supplies a **myomere** (**myotome** or **muscle plate**); however, the nerves that supply the limbs become larger and more complicated by branching and reuniting with one another. In this manner **plexuses** are formed not only in the limbs but also to many of the internal organs. The nerve fibers forming the plexuses are spoken of as **anastomosing** with one another. Blood vessels also **anastomose.** Moreover by counting the number of basic nerves that supply a limb, one has some idea as to the number of **mesodermal somites,** or muscle plates, that go into its embryological development. The various muscles supplied by the branches of the same nerve are believed to have originated from the same mesodermal somite.

NERVES OF BRACHIAL PLEXUS (Fig. 71)

Bisect and reflect the pectoralis muscles on both sides of the thorax and muscles of the neck. Identify the underlying arteries and veins as shown in Fig. 71 and as previously observed. The **cervical nerves I** to **V** branch from the spinal cord and supply only the neck. The ventral branches of the cervical nerves VI, VII, and VIII together with the first thoracic come from the spinal cord and anastomose to form the brachial plexus of the shoulder. From this plexus nerves supply the shoulder, forelimb, and thoracic wall. Leave the nerves and blood vessels in position but pull away the fat and connective tissue surrounding them so that they may be identified.

Near the cephalic edge of these laterally extending nerves of the brachial plexus are the arteries of the thyrocervical axis (Fig. 57) and the **transverse scapular vein** and **artery** (Fig. 52). Posterior to these are the **subscapular vein, axillary,** and the **subclavian,** or **axillary, vein** in the order named. Much time and patience are required to make a satisfactory dissection of the brachial plexus. Take up each nerve as described from its base to the structures it supplies to be sure that it is accurately identified. The student should be able to demonstrate any particular nerve to the instructor. If the work is done thoughtfully, some variations from the descriptions will be observed.

The following nerves are to be identified (the numbers 1 to 13 on Fig. 71 are simply for convenience).

1. The **suprascapular nerve** is the most anterior of the brachial plexus group; it comes from cervical nerve VI and extends over the anterior edge of the scapula to supply the supraspinatus muscle. Locate

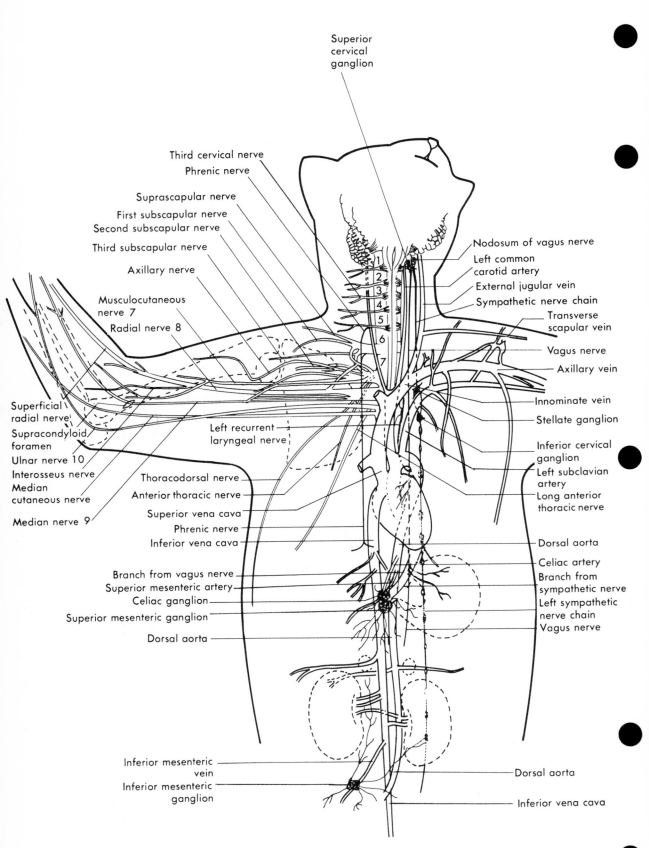

Fig. 71. Right brachial plexus, left sympathetic; trunk and vagus nerve, ventral view.

the upper edge of the scapula with a dissecting needle. The nerve is closely associated with the arteries of the thyrocervical axis.

2. The **anterior (first subscapular) nerve** arises from the sixth and seventh cervicals posterior to and parallel with the suprascapular nerve. It can be identified as it enters the anterior portion of the subscapular muscle.

3. The **middle (second subscapular) nerve** arises from the seventh cervical and supplies the posterior portion of the subscapular muscle and the teres major.

4. The **posterior (third subscapular) nerve** arises from cervical nerves VII and VIII. It has few branches and supplies the latissimus dorsi muscle.

5. The **phrenic nerve** is often included with the brachial plexus. It originates from the bases of cervical nerves V and VI as two slender roots that unite and pass into the thoracic cavity ventral to the base of the lungs to supply the diaphragm. Find it at the base of the lung and trace it both ways.

The question might arise concerning why the phrenic nerve should originate at the place where it does and pass through the thoracic cavity to get to the diaphragm. Why should it not originate from nerves of the lower thoracic region close to the diaphragm? The explanation is that the diaphragm (septum transversum) in the young embryo is in the region of the bases of the sixth and seventh cervical nerves, and when these nerves grow out, they become attached to the diaphragm. Then later, when the diaphragm migrates down past the thoracic region, it takes the phrenic nerves along with it. This explanation also applies to man.

6. The **axillary nerve** arises from cervical nerves VI and VII, is rather small, and extends laterally between the teres major and subscapularis muscles. It continues behind the head of the humerus and supplies the lateral head of the triceps and spinodeltoid muscles.

7. The **musculocutaneous nerve** arises from cervical nerves VI and VII, continues to the shoulder close to the coracobrachialis muscle, passes down the dorsal surface of the biceps, and continues on to the brachialis anticus and to the skin of the forearm.

8. The **radial nerve** is the largest of all the nerves in this region, and its base is dorsal to several smaller nerves. It also lies dorsal to the axillary artery and has two short roots from cervical nerves VII and VIII. It supplies the median surface of the large head of the triceps. It then passes laterally between the humerus and the first part of the median head of the triceps to the brachialis anticus muscle, where it divides into the **superficial radial** and the **interosseus**, previously identified when dissecting the muscles (see Fig. 30).

9. The **median nerve** can be identified because it has three long roots that unite at the same level as the head of the humerus. It was formerly identified as passing through the **supracondyloid foramen.**

10. The **ulnar nerve** is the largest of the remaining nerves. It usually lies close to the axillary and brachial arteries. It is the most posterior of the nerves that extend down the brachium to the elbow. It passes posterior to the supracondyloid foramen and across the olecranon process to the flexor carpi ulnaris muscle and other muscles of the forearm.

11. The **median cutaneous nerve** arises from the first thoracic nerve and extends laterally close to the base of the ulnar nerve to the distal half of the brachium. Here it passes laterally to the epitrochlean muscle and finally to the skin on the ulnar side of the forearm.

12. There are two anterior thoracic nerves: Fig. 71, *A*, the **short anterior thoracic,** arises from the eighth cervical and passes ventrally close to the ventral thoracic artery and vein to supply the underside of the pectoralis major muscle; *B*, the **long anterior thoracic,** arises from the eighth cervical and the first thoracic nerves. It passes near the long thoracic artery to the underside of the pectoralis minor and lateral surface of the serratus anterior muscles. These nerves are small and extend through the loose connective tissue, and thus some difficulty may be encountered in their identification.

177

13. The **thoracodorsalis nerve** (posterior thoracic) arises from the seventh cervical and, after going through the body wall, is between the scalenus muscle and the first two ribs. Bisect the scalenus lateral to the third rib and find the nerve under the anterior portion. The nerve passes dorsally and caudally close against the lateral surface of the levator scapula and serratus anterior but on the median side of the latissimus dorsi.

Some of the internal organs and several blood vessels are shown in Fig. 71 for orientation purposes. These have been previously discussed and identified. Color the arteries, veins, and nerves red, blue, and green, respectively.

The **thoracolumbar sympathetic nervous system** is dissected here because of its close association with the structures just dissected, but it will be considered again later. It consists of the ganglionated nerve chains, or trunks, their branches, plexuses, and many small ganglia. Dissect away the thin peritoneum from the left thoracic wall, about a centimeter lateral to the spinal column. The nerve chain may be seen as a fine white line behind the peritoneum. The ganglia are small enlargements on the nerve chain, and from them small, radiating fibers extend into the body wall and also into the spinal cord in the region of each segment. Dissect out the **left nerve trunk** forward to the **inferior cervical ganglion,** which is immediately posterior to the **subclavian artery.** A nerve fiber passes forward on each side of this artery to the **median cervical ganglion,** which is smaller and more median in position. Because of its shape, this is also called the **stellate ganglion.** Continue to dissect carefully the nerve trunk, or chain, forward as it passes dorsal to the **innominate vein** and turns more median to come into close association with the **vagus nerve,** forming the **vasosympathetic trunk.** Both are in the same connective tissue sheath. This trunk continues to the upper region of the neck to what appears to be one large ganglion. Separate the sympathetic trunk from the vagus nerve and also the two parts of this apparently single, large ganglion. The larger is the **nodosum**

of the vagus, and the smaller is the **superior cervical** of the **sympathetic nerve chain.**

Dissect out the sympathetic nerve trunk in the region of the diaphragm and find the **great splanchnic nerve fibers** going to the **large celiac,** or **semilunar, ganglion** and the **superior mesenteric ganglia** in the dorsal mesentery close to the bases of the **celiac** and **superior mesenteric arteries.** From these ganglia many fine nerve fibers branch to most of the abdominal viscera, and together they constitute the solar plexus. Dissect out the nerve chain posterior to the kidneys and find the branching nerve fibers going to the **inferior mesenteric ganglion** close to the **inferior mesenteric vein.** The sympathetic nervous system transmits stimuli that accelerate the heart, constrict blood vessels of the skin, inhibit the gastrointestinal activity, and dilate the bronchi.

The vagus nerve is not a part of the sympathetic nervous system but is closely associated with it, and hence its branches should be dissected out at this time. The vagus is a cranial nerve arising from the medulla oblongata and supplying the heart, lungs, stomach, and small intestines. In the early embryo the aforementioned organs are ventral to the medulla, and the vagus branches become attached to these organs; as they migrate down into the thoracic and abdominal cavities, they take these nerve endings along with them. This explanation is much the same as that for the phrenic nerve and the diaphragm, and it applies equally for cat and man.

Color arteries, veins, and nerves red, blue, and green, respectively, in Fig. 71.

NERVES OF LUMBAR PLEXUS (Fig. 72)

Since the pubic bones have been separated at the symphysis, dissect off the urinary bladder, urethra, and rectum from their attachments in the lumbar and sacral regions and reflect them anteriorward. Remove the arteries and veins from this region and carefully dissect away the muscles and connective tissue until the bases of the nerves are exposed as they come from the vertebrae.

Identify the centra of the fourth to the

178

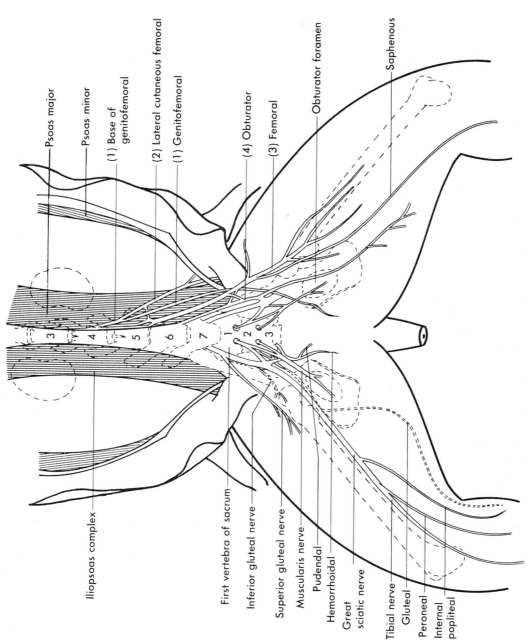

Psoas major

Psoas minor

(1) Base of genitofemoral

(2) Lateral cutaneous femoral

(1) Genitofemoral

(4) Obturator

(3) Femoral

Obturator foramen

Saphenous

Iliopsoas complex

First vertebra of sacrum

Inferior gluteal nerve

Superior gluteal nerve

Muscularis nerve

Pudendal

Hemorrhoidal

Great sciatic nerve

Tibial nerve

Gluteal

Peroneal

Internal popliteal

Fig. 72. Lumbar and sacral plexuses with psoas minor muscle displaced.

seventh lumbar vertebrae. Lateral to these are the psoas major and psoas minor muscles, which lie ventral to the transverse processes of the lumbar vertebrae. Dissect off the thin and more ventral psoas minor muscle and pull it laterally, as shown in Fig. 72. The following are the four principal nerves in the lumbar plexus.

1. The **genitofemoral** is a small nerve that arises in the region of the fourth lumbar vertebra. Its base is dorsal to the **psoas minor muscle,** which is close to the spinal column, but emerges and may be seen passing caudolaterally ventral to the **psoas major muscle.** The psoas minor muscles are shown pulled to the sides in Fig. 72. The genitofemoral nerve leaves the body anterior and lateral to the posterior ends of these muscles and supplies the craniomedian surface of the thigh, the adjacent abdominal wall, and the external genitalia.

2. The **lateral femoral cutaneous nerve** has its base in common with the genitofemoral nerve but divides dorsal to the **psoas minor muscle;** usually it receives a second root from the region of the fifth lumbar vertebra and passes caudolaterally. Identify it posterior and somewhat parallel to the genitofemoral. It crosses the psoas major muscle close to the **iliopsoas artery** and with it passes through the body wall. It supplies the anterior and lateral surface of the thigh.

3. The **femoralis nerve** is large and usually is seen without much dissection near the posterior limit of the body cavity as it enters the thigh. It is formed from the fifth and sixth lumbar nerves dorsal to the psoas minor muscle. It usually passes through the posterior portion of this muscle at the place where it enters the thigh. The femoral nerve lies anterior to the femoral artery as it enters the thigh but soon gives off the **long saphenous branch,** which accompanies the saphena artery and vein close to the median caudal surface of the thigh.

4. The **obturator nerve** arises from the sixth and seventh lumbar nerves. It is almost as large but much shorter than the femoral, and its proximal portion is parallel to it. It usually lies lateral and dorsal to the common iliac artery and vein. It passes back median to the innominate bone to the anterior edge of the **obturator foramen** and passes out through it to the obturator externus muscle, where it divides to supply the upper ends of the adductor femoris, pectineus, and gracilis muscles.

NERVES OF SACRAL PLEXUS (Fig. 72)

There are several nerves involved in the sacral plexus, but only six of the principal ones will be considered here. As you dissect, you will probably see several anastomosing fibers not mentioned in this discussion. Observe carefully the exact place where they are and add them to Fig. 72 where you are able without spending too much time.

1. The **great sciatic nerve** was observed when dissecting the muscles of the hip and thigh (Figs. 36 and 41), but its origin for the right leg is now to be dissected out from the ventral surface.

Dissect off the muscles and connective tissue from the ventral surface of the last lumbar vertebra and the sacrum. The sciatic is the largest of the nerves of the group and arises mostly from the sixth and seventh lumbar and first sacral nerve roots. These unite with other small fibers to form the lumbosacral cord. Before following the greater sciatic farther, some of the smaller branches near its base are to be considered.

2. The **superior gluteal nerve** is quite small and short. It arises from the lumbosacral part of the spinal cord and passes between the last lumbar vertebra and the tip of the ilium. It now passes ventral to the transverse process of the first sacral vertebra and dorsal to the ilium to supply the gluteus medius and minimus, the gemellus superior, and the pyriformis muscles. These nerve fibers are most distinct median and dorsal to the ilium.

3. The **inferior gluteal nerve** arises from a portion of the first sacral nerve and some fibers from the lumbosacral cord. It branches near the head of the femur and supplies the caudofemoralis and gluteus maximus muscles. Find the branches of the nerve on these muscles and then trace them back to the spinal column as far as you can.

Return to the great sciatic nerve at the place where it passes dorsal to the greater sciatic notch of the ilium. Turn the cat so that you can observe the lateral surface of the right leg. Find the sciatic and the place where it gives off a fairly large muscular branch to the inner surfaces of the upper portions of the biceps femoris, semitendinosus, and semimembranosus muscles. The sciatic passes down median to the biceps femoris and gives off more muscular branches and the long, slender **suralis.** The latter extends down the posterior surface of the gastrocnemius muscle to the foot. The sciatic nerve branches in the popliteal space into (a) the more lateral **peroneal,** which passes along the median surface of the lower end of the biceps and the lateral surface of the lateral head of the gastrocnemius and (b) the **tibial,** which passes median to the plantaris and between the median and lateral heads of the gastrocnemius.

4. The **small sciatic nerve (lesser sciatic, or cutaneus femoris posterior)** originates from the first, second, and third sacral nerves. It is small and has few branches. It comes to the lateral surface between the upper ends of the caudofemoralis and the biceps femoris. It crosses lateral to the biceps and supplies the skin of the posterior surface of the thigh close to the saphena parva vein. It also supplies the fat lateral to the base of the tail. Return to the ventral view of the pelvic region for the following nerve.

5. The **pudendus nerve** arises from the second and third sacral nerves, which unite lateral to the first caudal vertebra, and sometimes fine fibers from the lumbosacral cord join it also. It then turns medially to supply the external genitalia and tissues lateral to the rectum. It is larger and more distinct than the gluteal nerves.

6. The **hemorrhoidal nerve** is a branch of the pudendus and supplies the muscles and walls of the rectum and anus. There are other small fibers of the sacral plexus that are not considered to be of significance for this manual.

AUTONOMIC NERVOUS SYSTEM
(Figs. 71 and 74)

"Autonomic" means acting independently of volition. The autonomic nervous system regulates the involuntary reflexes especially concerned with nutritive, vascular, and reproductive activities. We can get only a general idea of this system in gross dissection since most of the nerve fibers and ganglia are small and require a special technique to identify. There are two main divisions: (1) **thoracolumbar** and (2) **craniosacral.**

(1) The **thoracolumbar** (sympathetic) **division** (previously mentioned) consists of nerve fibers that arise from the spinal cord from the thoracic and lumbar regions (see Fig. 74) and pass laterally on each side to the sympathetic nerve cord or trunk, about a centimeter from the spinal column. From here one group of fibers goes to the cutaneous blood vessels and sweat glands and the other group to the heart, lungs, and the various organs of the digestive and urogenital systems. In the abdominal cavity some of these fibers pass through the celiac, superior, or inferior mesenteric ganglia (Figs. 71 and 74).

(2) The **craniosacral** (parasympathetic) **nerve fibers** arise from one of two groups, either from the brain or from the spinal cord in the sacral region. Those fibers from the brain are parts of the third, seventh, ninth, tenth, and eleventh cranial nerves, and in the sacral region they are from the second, third, and fourth sacral nerves. In man the group from the brain comes from the third, seventh, ninth, and tenth only, while in the sacral region they are from the second, third, and fourth, the same numbered nerves as in the cat. These nerves are characterized by having ganglia on or near each organ supplied.

To a certain degree the **thoracolumbar** and the **craniosacral nerves** oppose one another in the effect of their stimuli. The former usually stimulates or increases the action of the parts supplied, while the latter usually relaxes or depresses the action of the organ; however, there are exceptions, and the reverse is true. For more detailed information, consult a good textbook on physiology.

SPINAL CORD AND SPINAL NERVES
(Fig. 74)

Remove the muscles dorsal to the vertebral column. Then with the bone forceps cut away the neural arches of the vertebrae

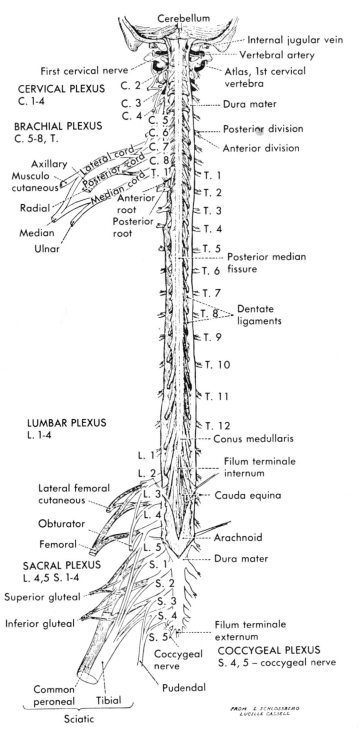

Fig. 73. Human spinal cord and spinal nerves. The dura mater has been opened to show the spinal cord and nerve roots. Plexuses are represented diagrammatically; only the main branches are shown. (From Millard, N. D., King, B. G., and Showers, M. J.: Human anatomy and physiology, Philadelphia, 1956, W. B. Saunders Co.)

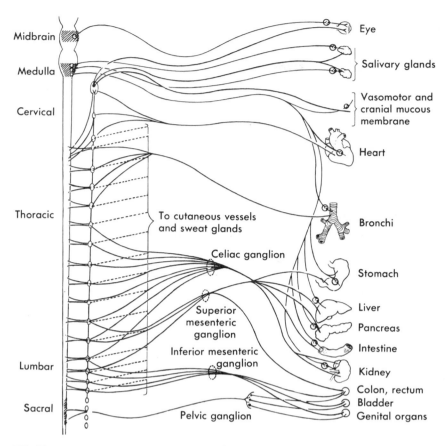

Midbrain

Medulla

Cervical

Thoracic

Lumbar

Sacral

To cutaneous vessels
and sweat glands

Celiac ganglion

Superior
mesenteric
ganglion

Inferior mesenteric
ganglion

Pelvic ganglion

Eye

Salivary glands

Vasomotor and
cranial mucous
membrane

Heart

Bronchi

Stomach

Liver

Pancreas

Intestine

Kidney

Colon, rectum

Bladder

Genital organs

Fig. 74. The autonomic nervous system. (After Meyer and Gottlieb, from Francis, C. C.: Introduction to human anatomy, ed. 5, St. Louis, 1968, The C. V. Mosby Co.)

so as to expose the spinal cord for its entire length, beginning at the foramen magnum.

Study the size of the cord at different levels. The thickening at the level of the anterior limbs is called the **cervical enlargement.** Notice how the cord becomes more slender in the **thoracic** region and then broadens again in the **lumbar enlargement.** Find the small filament, the **filum terminale,** in which the cord ends. Make a dorsal view drawing to show the foregoing parts

Observe the cut end of the cord under the compound microscope. Identify the gray matter, disposed in an **H**-shaped form in the interior, and the white matter lying outside it. Find the ventral median fissure extending lengthwise along the cord on its ventral side and the median dorsal septum joining the dorsal line.

Remove the neural arches from the sides

of the cord sufficiently to expose the origin of the **spinal nerves.** Find that each nerve arises from two roots, **dorsal** and **ventral,** and that these unite with each other to form the nerve a short distance from the cord. Find a prominent rounded swelling on the dorsal root just before it unites with the ventral root; this is called the **sensory ganglion.** Notice the manner in which each of the roots arises from the cord.

Note that the nerves in the anterior region of the body leave the cord nearly at right angles and that those in the posterior region come to lie almost parallel to the cord, which is drawn out into a fine, elongated structure posterior to the seventh lumbar vertebra, and are called the filum terminale. The filum terminale and the sacral nerves, which lie somewhat parallel and within the neural arches, together constitute the cauda equina.

SOME DIFFERENCES IN PLEXUSES AND NERVES OF CAT AND MAN

1. In man the fifth, sixth, seventh, and eighth cervical nerves, with the first thoracic, form the brachial plexus, whereas in the cat it is the same except that the fifth cervical is not included.

2. In man the third, fourth, and fifth cervical nerves go to form the phrenic plexus, whereas in the cat the fifth and sixth form it.

3. The lumbosacral plexus is formed in the cat by the last four lumbar nerves and three sacral, whereas in man three and one-half lumbar nerves and four sacral nerves form it.

4. The long thoracic nerve in man is considered homologous with the posterior thoracic nerve of the cat, since both supply the serratus anterior muscle.

5. There are thirty-eight pairs of spinal nerves in the cat and thirty pairs in man. They are arranged as follows:

	Cervical	Thoracic	Lumbar	Sacral	Caudal
Cat	8	12	7	3	7-8
Man	8	12	5	5	0

6. The phrenic nerve in man is formed from the contribution of the third, fourth, and fifth cervical nerves, whereas in the cat the fifth and sixth cervical nerves make this contribution.

REVIEW QUESTIONS ON SPINAL NERVES AND PLEXUSES

1. What are the principal parts of the sympathetic nervous system? (Figs. 71, 72, and 73)

2. Name the three plexuses that supply the limbs of a cat. (Figs. 71 and 72)

3. Name the principal nerves of the brachial plexus. (Figs. 71 and 73)

4. Name the principal nerves of the lumbar and the sacral plexus. (Figs.72 and 73)

5. What do the bases of the principal nerves of each plexus indicate concerning the number of myomeres that went into the formation of each of the paired limbs?

6. What are the principal parts of the parasympathetic nervous system? Where are they located?

7. Explain about the phrenic nerve and the migration of the diaphragm from its position in the embryo. (Fig. 71)

8. Name three large ganglia in the neck and thorax. (Fig. 71)

9. What is the real distinction of the vertebral and the neural canal in a vertebra?

9

General summary

This book is intended to present a method of study of the anatomy of the cat and of man, when the human cadaver is not available for dissection, as a preparation for an exacting course in human anatomy in medical and dental schools. The main object is not to analyze or interpret the significance of the differences in the anatomy of these two animals; however, several generalizations have been reached, not all of which have convincing proof.

When comparing this carnivore and this primate, we find highly specialized anatomical systems in each, but in different directions—one with the body carried in a more primitive horizontal position and the other in an erect position. This difference appears to be the first main factor in effecting the variations and adaptations in all anatomical systems. The animal with the horizontal body position has the advantage of developing more speed than the one with the erect position. The latter, however, has the forelimbs free for defense, for obtaining food, and for taking food to the mouth in suitable amounts and conditions.

The second main factor in the divergence of these two animals is the enlargement and specialization of the brain. The enlargement forced the skull dorsalward and the nose, jaws, and eyes, ventralward. As a result the eyes could be turned to different horizontal positions by rotating the head or skull on the first vertebra, and likewise the first on the second, without bending the cervical vertebrae from side to side.

This ability to rotate the head on the spinal column reduces the need for muscles to move the ears. Therefore the anterior and posterior auricular muscles, which are well developed in the ear, became vestigial, as they are in man.

The canine teeth of the cat are fitted for piercing and tearing flesh, not for chewing. These teeth are developed beyond efficient chewing function in the saber-toothed tiger (saber-toothed cat). Man's canine teeth are relatively small and not well fitted for piercing and tearing, which indicates that no recent ancestors of man followed this method of attack. The movements of the forelimbs of the cat are consistently parallel with the longitudinal vertical plane of the cat's body, and the cat does not need a large clavicle to brace the shoulder as does man, in whom there are movements of the arms from side to side. The coracoid process in both cat and man is a vestigial remnant of the large coracoid bone of reptiles, whereas in many reptiles and all birds the shoulder lacks a large, flat scapula for the attachment of muscles.

The long neural spines of the thoracic vertebrae, which project posteriorly, are believed to be in response to the pull of the muscles that support the head on the end of a fairly straight neck. These long neural spines are quite large in the cow and bison, in which the heads are large. The giraffe has an exceptionally long neck but a small head, and the neck is usually held at an angle; therefore the thoracic neural spines of the giraffe are relatively short. The erect position of man removes much of the pull on the muscles that support the head. The neural spines are relatively small, but their angle suggests that the ancestors may have had a horizontal body. In the neural spines of the four posterior thoracic vertebrae the spines project forward, as in the lumbar vertebrae also, and the transverse processes, because the pull of the muscles, are from the pelvic region. These long, anteriorly projecting transverse processes of the lumbar vertebrae indicate that their ancestors were tree climbers or leaping animals. These processes in herbivorous animals and in man project almost straight laterally, showing no signs of recent tree-climbing ancestors.

The sacrum of the cat contains a fusion of three vertebrae, but in man, where there is a greater strain in this region because of the erect position, there are five or seven fused vertebrae. In the bird, where the body is held in a semierect position, the strain is relatively greater, and the sacrum compensates by having a great many vertebrae fused with the innominates.

There are from four to twenty-six caudal vertebrae in the cat. The long tail with many vertebrae is probably correlated with the ability to run fast. The cheetah, which is noted for its swiftness in running, has an unusually long tail, which is believed to aid in keeping balance when running rapidly. This suggests that the ancestors of the cat were fast runners, and we know that the cat has not lost this ability. The caudal vertebrae of man are reduced to from three to five vertebrae that are more or less fused with one another. Sometimes in the human female there are extra vertebrae, or they curve forward, reducing the size of the birth canal, and interfere with the passage of the young at the time of parturition. Cesarean operations are sometimes advised because of this condition. The birth canal is relatively larger in the cat and not so constricted, and parturition is apparently less difficult.

The horizontal position of the body is much better for the support of the intestines, because the dorsal mesentery extends from them to the spinal column. In the erect position the intestines settle or sag down toward the pelvis, constricting or impinging upon the urinary and reproductive systems. Circulative and digestive functions of the intestines are curtailed, and the abdomen tends to protrude.

The erect position in man makes a greater strain on the heart because of the pull of gravity on the blood in most of the veins and on the lymph in the lymphatic vessels. The ankles and calves of the legs often swell in man past middle age, resulting largely from lack of normal lymph circulation. The best rest or relief is obtained when lying down.

The covering of hair on the cat is definitely suited for outdoor life. Man compensates for the lack of hair over the body by wearing clothes, and in cold weather he feels the need of a heavy fur coat. Many of man's anatomical structures and his instinct suggest the need for outdoor life.

The anatomical specializations of the cat are no doubt better adapted for a life in the wilds of nature than those of man for a life in the city. The cat has apparently permitted itself to be partially domesticated because the life is less strenuous. The teeth, the claws, the keen sense of hearing and sight, the strong muscles for swift motion and locomotion, and the ability to digest and live on many kinds of food contribute to the general ability to get along quite successfully without the aid of man. The efficiency of these anatomical structures shows the ability to respond positively to the "call of the wild." The cat has reserve anatomical equipment for offense and defense. The cat shows ability to adapt itself to many conditions of the environment and therefore has strong promise for many future generations.

Man is a highly specialized primate and shows adaptations of many systems that are not exactly the best for the life now led by a great number of human beings. The greatest specialization in intellectual ability appears at present to be in the development of tools of defense and offense and in trips to the moon rather than in developing new methods for the production of more food with less effort. Better methods are needed for the prevention or alleviation of illness and poverty and for the development of better moral standards.

There are several strong reasons for the final statements, as follows: 1. There are many vestigial organs in cat and man. 2. There are many examples of recapitulation that can be demonstrated. 3. The validity of the existence of vestigial organs and the occurrence of recapitulation has not been seriously questioned. 4. There has not been a more logical or reasonable explanation than the following statements: (a) Vestigial organs are degenerated structures that were more useful and usually relatively larger in lower and possibly ancestral forms. (b) Recapitulation has occurred, continues to occur, and can be demonstrated. From these reasons it is therefore concluded that (1) the cat and man are each highly specialized but in different directions and (2) vestigial organs and recapitulation are interpreted as supporting the belief that the cat and man are what they are structurally largely because of dozens of anatomical changes, which have occurred during the many years of ancestral generations and are largely due to the laws of heredity, response to the environment, and mutation.

GENERAL REVIEW QUESTIONS

1. Explain and give an example of recapitulation.

2. Explain two anomalies you have observed on the cat.

3. What are the two main parts of the pituitary, or hypophysis.

4. What is the sympathetic nerve chain or trunk? (Fig. 71)

5. What anatomic structures of the embryo, or of adult man, suggest a more primitive ancestry?

6. What duct drains each of the following body structures? (a) parotid salivary gland, (b) liver, (c) urinary bladder, and (d) gallbladder. (Fig. 47, *B*)

7. Why is man sometimes called a mechanical misfit?

8. Do the facts of embryology help in the interpretation of the structure of adult cat or man?

9. Explain the general function of the hepatic portal system and the liver.

10. Explain the "gorilla" rib in man.

11. State some of the evidence which causes many scientists to believe that man, in his body frame, bears the indelible imprint of his lowly ancestors.

12. State the exact location of the true and the false vocal cords. (Fig. 62)

13. What relation is the ear to the embryonic gill clefts?

14. Name the two bladders of the cat and the duct that drains each. (Figs. 47, *B* and 48)

15. From what embryological structures are the cartilages of the larynx and the bones of the middle ear formed?

16. Why is the urethra of the male truly a urogenital duct, while the female urethra is not? (Figs. 48 and 51)

17. What is a hormone? Where is it produced? (See definition of terms.)

18. Examine several cats and sketch the variations of the branches of the innominate, carotid, and subclavian arteries as they put off from the aortic arch.

19. How does the ear function in maintaining the balance?

20. Examine the hepatic portal system of five cats and sketch the variations in the way the main branches join one another.

21. Name five glands and their secretions that aid in digestion.

Definitions of terms

abduction the act of turning outward; a movement away from the midline.

abductor applied to a muscle that draws a structure away from the median line or from a neighboring part or limb.

acetabulum a socket in each innominate bone of the pelvis that receives the head of the femur.

adduction a movement toward the median plane of the body.

adductor applied to a muscle that draws a structure toward the median axis.

adipose of a fatty nature; fat.

adjacent lying near or close to; contiguous.

adrenal an endocrine gland situated near the kidney.

adrenalin a secretion of the adrenal or suprarenal gland.

adventitia the outer coat of an artery or tubular structure.

afferent to; carry to.

alimentary pertaining to digestion or to the digestive canal.

allantois an embryonic diverticulum from the hindgut.

alveolus the socket of a tooth.

amnion an embryonic sac enclosing the embryo.

analogy similar in function; without identity.

anastomose a communication or network between blood vessels or nerves.

anatomy the science of the structure of the animal body and the relation of the parts.

anlage the primordium or first part of a differentiating part of a structure.

anomaly a marked variation from the normal standard.

anterior situated in front of or in the forward part of; toward the head end.

aponeurosis heavy fascia, white gristly membrane, serving mainly as an investment for muscle; flat tendon.

appendix an outgrowth or process.

artery a blood vessel that carries blood away from the heart.

articulation place where one solid part rubs against another.

atavistic inheritance of a character from a grandparent or remote ancestor.

atrophied shrunken; having undergone diminution in size.

azygous having no fellow; unpaired.

back behind or toward the rear; the side of the trunk nearest the spinal column.

bilateral symmetry an arrangement of parts or organs in such a manner that the corresponding structures are similar on the two sides.

biology the science that deals with living creatures.

biopsy inspection of the living body or a piece removed therefrom.

bisect to divide or cut into two parts.

brachium the upper arm; shoulder to elbow.

branchial arches the cartilages or bones that lie lateral to the pharynx.

branchial pouches the outpocketings, or diverticulae, of the lateral walls of the embryonic pharynx.

bulb a rounded mass or part; an enlargement.

bulbourethral gland Cowper's gland, a secreting organ in the wall of the duct that drains the urinary bladder, near the base of the penis.

bulla a dilated or rounded part of the wall of a cavity.

bursa a sac or saclike cavity.

cadaver the human body after death; a corpse.

calyx a cup-shaped organ or cavity; a recess or pelvis of the kidney.

capillaries the minute blood or lymph vessels.

cartilage gristle, a white elastic substance attached to a bone; a precursor of bone.

caudad an adverb meaning posterior to or away from the head.

caudal an adjective meaning tailward or posterior.

cell theory the belief that all organisms are single cells or organizations of cells.

central of or pertaining to the middle point, lines, or plane; toward the center.

cephalic toward the head.

cervix the constricted area between the vagina and the body of the uterus.

chondrocranium the cartilaginous skull.

chorion one of the three embryonic membranes.

chorion frondosum a part of the chorion that forms the embryonic portion of the placenta.

chyle the milky fluid absorbed by the lacteals of the lymph system in the wall of the intestines.

chyme a thick, grayish liquid mass into which food is converted by gastric juice.

circumflex bend about; curved like a bow.

cochlea the spiral portion of the inner ear that contains the epithelial nerve endings of the sense of hearing.

concha shell, as pinna of ear.

connective tissue the cells that bind together and support the various structures of the body.

cornu any hornlike projection.

cranial an adjective pertaining to the head or skull, or in the direction of the head, or anteriorward.

crest a projecting ridge.

cyst a sac or bladder that contains a liquid.

deep away from the surface.

diencephalon the second lobe of the brain.

differentiation the process by which a cell or group of cells becomes unlike in structure or function from what it was.

dissect to separate or cut apart for anatomical study.

distal remote, farthest from the center or origin, as opposed to proximal; away from the beginning.

dorsad an adverb meaning the same as dorsal.

dorsal an adjective referring to the back or upper surface as opposed to the ventral or lower surface.

ductus deferens (wolffian duct) the excretory duct of the testis.

ectomy to remove from the body.

efferent outgoing from a center as opposed to afferent.

embryo the fetus in its earlier stages of development, especially before the end of the third month of gestation.

embryology the science that deals with the development of the fetus from the egg.

endochondral developed within cartilage.

endocrine secreting internally into the blood or lymph; a substance that modifies metabolism.

endoderm (entoderm) one of the primitive germ layers that gives rise to the embryo.

endometrium mucosal lining of the uterus.

endothelial the thin lining of blood or lymph vessels.

enzyme a chemical ferment formed by living cells.

epaxial situated above or upon the axis.

epidermis the outermost, nonvascular layer of the skin.

epigenesis the theory that development starts from a structureless cell.

epiglottis the cartilaginous covering for the opening from the pharynx into the larynx.

epimysium the sheath surrounding a muscle.

epiphysis a dorsal projection from the roof of the diencephalon; a part of a long bone next to the joint.

epithelium a thin layer of cells of an inner or outer surface of the body.

excretion a substance thrown off from the body.

exocrine secreting outwardly, as opposed to endocrine.

extension a movement whereby two parts become farther apart.

external refers to the outer surface as opposed to the central part.

extrinsic having origin outside of an organ or limb.

facet any small plane surface, as where one bone rubs against another.

fascia a sheet of tissue that invests and connects muscles.

fat an oily substance that covers connective tissue.

feces the excrement; the intestinal discharge.

fecundity the ability to produce offspring.

fertilization the fusion of sperm and egg.

fetus the unborn offspring of a viviparous animal after the end of the third month.

flexion a movement or bend, as at a joint.

foramen a hole or perforation.

foramen cecum a pit on the base of the tongue where the thyroid gland originated.

foramen ovale an opening between the atria or in the sphenoid bone.

fossa a depression or hollow.

front the foremost part in locomotion.

fusiform tapering from the center to both ends.

gamete a mature germ cell.

ganoids a group or subclass of fishes.

ganglion a mass of nerve cells that serves as a center of nervous influence.

gene a unit of hereditary or germinal factor.

genetics the science that deals with the origin of the characteristics of an individual.

gill cleft same as gill slit; an opening to the outside from the pharynx.

gland an organ that separates any fluid from the blood.

glottis the opening from the pharynx into the larynx.

glycogen a form of carbohydrate or starch stored in the liver.

gonad a reproductive gland, as the ovary or testis.

great or greater omentum a fold of dorsal mesentery attached to the greatest curvature of the stomach.

groin place where the hind leg joins the body.

harderian gland a degenerated lacrimal secreting organ of the eye.

hemal pertaining to the blood.

hepatic pertaining to the liver.

hermaphrodite an animal that has parts of both male and female reproductive organs.

hernia a protrusion of an anatomical structure through an abnormal opening.

histology a discourse on the minute or cell structure of a tissue or organ.

homology a similarity in origin and structure.

hormone a chemical substance produced in an organ, absorbed and carried by the blood to some distant organ that it excites to a different action.

hypaxial situated ventral to the body axis.

hypophysis same as pituitary; an endocrinal gland ventral to the brain.

hypothesis a tentative theory; a supposition.

ileum the third division of the small intestine.

ilium the anterior portion of the innominate bone.

inferior toward the lower end; away from the head.

infra beneath some structure or position.

inguinal pertaining to the groin.

innominate without a name; nameless.

insertion the place of attachment of a muscle to be moved; the more distal end.

insulin an endocrine secretion of the pancreas.

intermediate between two other structures.

internal refers to the central or deepest part.

intrinsic situated internally; with or pertaining only to one part.

irritability the quality of responding to a stimulus.

Jacobson's organ a vestigial structure in the septum of the nose; the vomeronasal organ.

jejunum the second division of the small intestine.

karyokinesis mitosis; indirect cell division.

katabolism destructive metabolism; a throwing down.

lacteals lymph capillaries that absorb fat from the wall of the small intestines.

larynx the voice box or Adam's apple.

lateral to the side of a median plane away from the midline of the body.

lesser omentum a part of the ventral mesentery attached to the concave surface of the stomach.

leukocyte a white blood corpuscle.

ligament a form of connective tissue that joins one bone to another.

linea alba a white or median line down the front of the abdomen.

litter the number of young born at one time from the same parent.

loculus a small space or cavity.

lymph a transparent, slightly yellow liquid that arises from the blood and functioning protoplasm.

malleolus a little hammer; a rounded process on either side of the ankle.

mammary pertaining to the milk-producing gland.

marsupium an external pouch in which the young are carried, as in the opossum or kangaroo.

mechanistic physical and chemical forces independent of any life processes.

Meckel's diverticulum a remnant of the yolk stalk attached to the ileum.

medial toward the midline of the body.

median toward the plane that vertically bisects an organism or part; the midline of the body.

mediastinum a space in the thorax between the two pleurae.

medulla the fifth or most posterior lobe of the brain.

mendelism the law that an offspring is not intermediate in type between its parents but one or the other is predominant.

meninges the membranes covering the brain.

mesoderm the middle primitive embryonic germ layer.

mesonephros the middle kidney or wolffian body.

mesothelium the lining of the body cavity.

metabolism the sum of all processes by which living substance is produced and maintained.

metamere a primitive segment or part.

metamerism a state of being in which the component parts are identical.

metanephros the hind kidney or that of adult man.

morphology the science that deals with the form of organized beings.

mucoid resembling mucus.

mucosa the thin tissue covering the organs of abdominal organs; visceral peritoneum.

mucus a viscid, watery secretion of the mucous glands. (The word "mucus" is a noun, and "mucous" is an adjective.)

myomere an embryonic muscular segment.

myotome a somite, a primitive mesodermal segment.

natural selection a theory devised by Darwin to explain how evolution operates.

navel the scar on the abdomen where the umbilical cord was attached in the embryonic stage.

nephridium a kidney tubule.

nephros a kidney.

neuraxis the brain and spinal cord.

obturator foramen an opening between the ischium and pubic bones in the pelvis.

odontoid process a toothlike projection on the axis.

omentum a double fold of peritoneum extending from the greater or the lesser curvature of the stomach.

ontogeny the development of a single individual organism from the egg.

oogenesis the origin and progressive development of the female germ cell.

organ any part of the body having a special function.

origin the beginning; the end closer to the median plane of the body; in a muscle the end that is the more stationary.

oviparous producing eggs or ova that are hatched outside the body.

parenchyma the essential or functional cells of an organ as distinguished from its stroma or framework.

parietal refers to the body wall.

parthenogenesis the development of an egg or ovum without fertilization.

parturition the act of giving birth to young.

pathology the science that deals with diseased tissue or organs.

pectoral girdle the various bones to which the anterior limbs or forelimbs are attached.

pelvic girdle the bones or the two innominates to which the posterior or hind limbs are attached.

peripheral close to the outer surface; away from the center.

peritoneum the thin, shiny lining of the body wall.

pharynx a section of the digestive tract between the mouth and esophagus.

phrenic related to the diaphragm.

phylogeny the history of a race or a group of plants or animals.

pinna the part of the ear that projects from the side of the head.

pituitary (hypophysis) a gland at the base of the brain.

placenta an organ of pregnancy through which nutriment and waste pass to and from the embryo.

plasma the fluid portion of the blood.

plexus a net or meshwork of nerves or blood vessels.

posterior behind or tailward; dorsal or back.

precursor one that precedes; a forerunner.

primordium the first part of a structure to form.

pronation a rotation, as in turning the palm downward or backward.

pronephros the earliest embryonic or head kidney.

prostate gland a secreting organ of the male near the upper end of the urethra.

protraction the pulling forward of a part.

proximal nearest to, relatively closer to the central portion, as opposed to distal; the beginning of a structure.

ramus a primary division of a bone, nerve, or blood vessel.

raphe a ridge, furrow, or line that marks the union of halves of various symmetrical structures.

reflect to turn back.

regeneration the renewal or repair of an injured or absent structure.

regurgitate spit up or vomit.

retraction the act of drawing back.

retroperitoneal behind the thin, shiny lining of the body cavity, as the location of kidneys or gonads.

sagittal resembling an arrow; straight; running in an anteroposterior direction.

scrotum a pouch that contains the testes.

sella turcica a Turkish saddle; a depression in the upper surface of the sphenoid bone, the pituitary fossa.

semen the fluid secreted by the testes and other glands that contains the sperm.

seminal vesicle an enlargement or receptacle for sperm near the wreathed end of the vas deferens or sperm duct.

shank the leg between the knee and ankle.

shin the front part of the leg below the knee.

sinus a recess; cavity.

somatic pertaining to the framework of the body, as distinguished from the viscera.

somite a primitive segment, a blocklike mass of mesodermal cells in a young embryo.

spermatogenesis the origin and development of the male germ cells.

spheniod wedge shaped; a bone at the base of the skull.

squamosal pertaining to a scale; the vertical plate of the temporal bone.

sternebrae the bony sections of the sternum.

stroma the tissue that forms the framework or matrix of an organ.

superficial pertaining to or near the surface.

superior higher or upper.

supination a movement by which palm or plantar surfaces are turned upward or inward, respectively.

suplnator applied to a muscle that turns the palm upward, as in rotation of forearm.

supra above; beyond.

sustentitial pertaining to supporting tissue or matrix.

system an association of organs for the performance of some general function of the body.

symphysis a line of junction or fusion of bones; originally distinct, often of corresponding parts.

tendon a form of connective tissue by which a muscle is attached to a bone.

tentorium a part of the dura mater separating the cerebrum from the cerebellum; sometimes ossifies.

testicle same as testis.

testis the male gonad where the sperm develop.

tissue a group of similar cells united in the performance of a special function.

transverse across; from one side to the other; often means a cross section.

trochanter either of the two processes below the neck of the femur.

tubercle a rough, round eminence on a bone.

tuberosity a broad eminence situated on a bone.

tympanum the eardrum.

umbilicus the navel; the scar on the abdomen that marks the place of attachment of the cord to the placenta.

urachus a ligament that extends from the urinary bladder to the navel.

ureter the duct that drains urine from the kidney to the urinary bladder.

urethra the duct or passageway from the urinary bladder to the exterior surface of the body.

uterus the womb or place of development of the embryo and fetus.

vagina masculinus (prostatic utricle) the remnant of the müllerian duct found in the male near the upper end of the urethra.

vasa efferentia the tubules that drain the testis.

vein a vessel that conveys blood toward the heart.

ventral pertaining to or situated on the abdomen.

ventricle any small cavity as applied to the heart or brain.

vermiform wormlike.

vertebra one of the bony sections or units of the spinal column.

vertebrae two or more of the bony sections of the spinal column.

vertebrate an animal that has a spinal column.

vesicle a small bladder or sac containing liquid.

vestigial pertaining to a remnant, rudimentary structure.

villus a minute vascular chorionic tuft.

viscera the large anterior organs of any of the four great cavities of the body, especially the abdomen.

viviparous bringing forth young alive.

wolffian duct sperm duct or vas deferens extending from the testis to the urethra.

xiphoid shaped like a sword; pertaining to the posterior portion of the sternum.

zygapophysis two or more processes yoked or joined, as in an articulating process.

zygomatic pertaining to the arch formed by the malar and temporal bones.